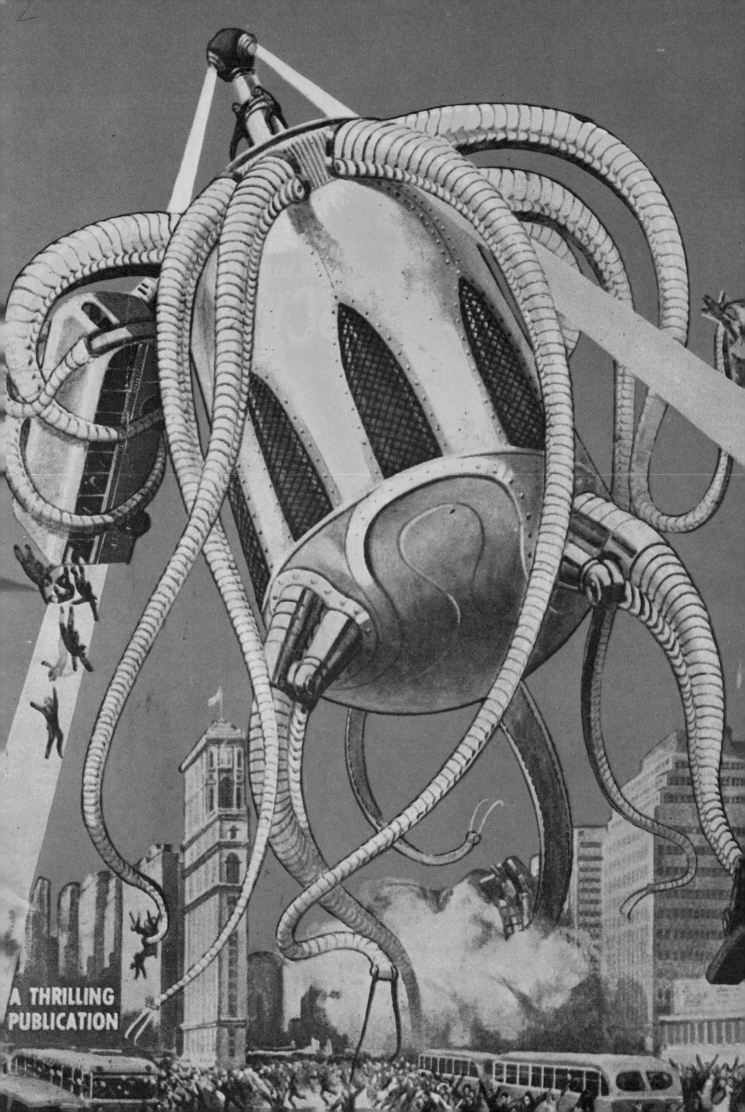

A THRILLING
PUBLICATION

ONE HUNDRED YEARS OF
SCIENCE FICTION
ILLUSTRATION
1840 ~ 1940

Anthony Frewin

BLOOMSBURY BOOKS
LONDON

JUPITER BOOKS (LONDON) LTD
167 Hermitage Road, London, N.4.

First published 1974.

**This edition published 1988 by
Bloomsbury Books an imprint of
Godfrey Cave Associates Limited
42 Bloomsbury Street, London WC1B 3QJ
under license from Minotaur Publishing Co Ltd**

ISBN 1 870630 521

Printed in Yugoslavia

The Gods, who haunt
The lucid interspace of world and world,
Where never creeps a cloud, or moves a wind,
Nor ever falls the least white star of snow,
Nor ever lowest roll of thunder moans,
Nor sound of human sorrow mounts to mar
Their sacred everlasting calm!

Alfred, Lord Tennyson.

CONTENTS

Thus thirty-one zillion dollars! Drawing by Elliott Dold from *Astounding*, June 1937.

INTRODUCTION

'Science Fiction? Yes, I used to read a lot of those magazines at one time. Quite enjoyed it too, but now there's not much demand for them I don't get the opportunity. At one time we used to have five or six different things each month. I used to put them up on the stand and they were never there more than a couple of days. It's a bit different today and I only get them to order. Still got a few regulars though and I look at their's when I can. Thing is they buy the books now, almost the same price, and you can put them up on your shelves at home, can't you? Not the same with magazines, eh?'

Thus a newsagent in north London who prides himself on reading nearly everything he sells. It was closing time late on a Friday and I had asked him whether he had a copy of *Analogue*. He had read his first SF magazine in the 1930s when 'kids still thought the inside of a wireless set was the most exciting thing they'd ever be likely to see', and they continued to be popular throughout the period as 'these Yank things gave you lots to think about along the same lines'. What was his definition of SF?

'Well, it's about the future mainly and what they're going to invent. The shape of things to come...exploring space and the stars. Life on other planets. All the things that could happen to us if we don't watch out! It used to get you thinking about the future alright! You take H. G. Wells. When we were kids we used to read a lot of him. His stories made you realise things were going to happen. Before I read all this I didn't think the future was anything more than getting an increase at work and settling down. Really I didn't. When we all saw *Things To Come* at St Helens we couldn't believe our eyes — that could be us in twenty years time! It was the thirties then and everybody lived a bit nearer the bone. Today it's all different. I'm like the rest of them I suppose...now'.

The newsagent's definition meets the bill for most people, but it is hardly a full definition. To go one step further we might say that SF is about the future in terms of science and technology and their inherent social implications.

Shying away from the semantic imbroglio of Higher Meaning, we will take it that a style of writing, and therefore of thought, does exist which readily admits to the appellation. That in the genre science plays an ideational role (often to the detriment of the story's characters and hence SF's delayed acceptance by academics and others raised on the humanistic concept of the novel), and that SF, as we now know it, is primarily a twentieth century phenomenon, is about all one can say before being assaulted by partisan critics.

Definitions are a tacky business. For instance, the Swedish writer, Sam Lundwall grapples for a succinct definition only to have it continually elude him at the beginning of his recent expositional study (*Science Fiction: What It's All About*, New York 1971, pps. 12-25). He describes the literature as

(ABOVE) An important New World contribution to the secret history of air travel (where reality is always several hundred years out of date). Patented by a Dr. Mariott, sometime of New York and Chicago, the *Avitor* of 1869 would have revolutionised the trans-Atlantic crossing and made the twentieth century world radically different from what we know had it only left the drawing board. The fact that it did not is comparatively unimportant. Like so many Victorian inventions never realised, it increased the vocabulary of the future, widened the range of possibilities, and served as feedback to the imaginative writers who had first suggested such a conception. Reality apes SF, and comes out a poor second.

giving a Sense of Wonder (a chief characteristic of Surrealism — *vide* André Breton. But we will not go into *that*!) and cannot successfully add more to the formulation. Finally he admits that there are probably as many definitions as there are readers, and, besides, he would like to replace the existing term with that of *Speculative* Fiction anyway! Modestly he declines to define the new term which one had hoped was chosen to facilitate explanation quite apart from allowing a wider selection of works to be grouped together.
Further along the critical ladder a more recent attempt was made by Brian Aldiss in his introductory history (*Billion Year Spree*, London 1974, pps. 8-10): 'Science fiction is the search for a definition of man and his status in the universe which will stand in our advanced but confused state of knowledge (science), and is characteristically cast in the Gothic or post-Gothic mould'. After further qualification and enlargement one feels the definition beginning to dissolve a little. Even the most cheap and artless pulp SF story can be interpreted as a 'search for the definition of man' (surely a fundamental striving of all literature anyway) but only in the sense that, say, *Little*

(BELOW) What an inventor like Dr. Mariott added to the storehouse of the future, an illustrator like Fred T. Jane would take out to embellish a work of imagination. In this engraving for E. Douglas Fawcett's *Hartmann the Anarchist* (1896) we see the very best that the present can offer in flight technology, the balloon,

Red Riding Hood might similarly be read. The phrase about 'advance knowledge' is really the rub, rescuing as it does SF from confusion with other forms and, as Aldiss rightly remarks, anchoring it in the NOW rather than the THEN. He also notes that many formulations fail because of their concentration on content and disregard for form, this is deftly dealt with by the use of the term Gothic. Nevertheless it is probably the nearest we will ever get to true and accurate definition, and the reader is urged to study Aldiss' full text closely.
At this stage one is tempted to suggest that we should, like the ubiquitous George Hay, have delegated the task to civic employees — *Science fiction is what you find on the shelves of public libraries marked science fiction!*
As to the origins of SF, here a realm is entered every bit as speculative as the writing itself. Depending on who you are and where your money goes, you might feel that SF began in classical Greece with Aristophanes' *The Birds*, with Kepler's *Dream* in the 1600s, with Mary Shelley's *Frankenstein* in 1819 (a current favourite), with Jules Verne or H. G. Wells in the late nineteenth century (both perennial favourites), or perhaps not until the term science fiction itself was evolved in the 1920s (the purist approach).
In discussing the pre- and early history of SF all we can do is point to writers,

being defeated with great ease by the Future, the powered airship. Eighteen years later during the Great War actuality would vie with this creation. Scenarios for the defence establishments of the world forever trying to insure themselves against what is yet to be. Thus the armaments race as a labour of Sisyphus.

Frank R. Paul's cover painting for *Wonder Stories*, June 1935.

Paul is easily the single greatest name in twentieth century science fiction art. His innovatory work set the tenor and supplied much of the vocabulary for the style of illustration we associate with the medium. It is only recently in the post-hallucinogen years that a break has been made with his conventions as SF has diluted its pre-occupation with technology by exploring the landscapes of the mind.

The story supplying the inspiration over thirty years ago was Lawrence Manning's pre-Triffid fantasy, 'Seeds from Space'.

such as those enumerated above, who dealt with themes and ideas, or employed methods of approach which resemble, partially or wholly, those of current practitioners in the genre. It is an open-ended debate which will continue as long as there is anyone about who continues to read it. The reader is referred to the volumes by Lundwall and Aldiss for a fuller discussion.

Significantly, the actual term science fiction first appeared in print at the birth of the genre's twentieth century development. It was used by an entrepreneur of monthly magazine publishing in America called Hugo Gernsback (of whom more later) in *Science Wonder Stories*, June 1929, one of his many publications. Gernsback, who played an important role in the development of the style, had translated the term literally from the German and used it to replace his earlier and uglier construction *scientifiction*, a contraction of scientific fiction, the rubric under which he had published stories in an earlier magazine, *Science and Invention*. Before this we encounter such terms as scientific romance and scientific fantasy, the former still being applied to H. G. Wells, and, on occasion, Jules Verne.

SF spent its formative years in American magazines with such names as *Amazing* and *Astounding*, all of which had a wide circulation that, initially, was restricted to the lower middle classes, manual and semi-skilled workers, and the teenagers (or rather their equivalent then) who defy divisioning. The crudely written stories were printed on even cruder paper (hence the term 'pulps'), and sold for a few nickels on every news-stand throughout the States. The early stories appear to us now as little more than *Boy's Own Paper* type yarns with a strong emphasis on gadgetry and similar rudimentary mechanics. It did not take long for the writing to secure an identity and, with it, a popularity and acceptance far beyond the country of its birth.

The present books aims at being a modest yet comprehensive collection of SF art from the century which began with the French illustrator Isidore Grandville in the 1840s and ended with the maturing of the cover art of the pulps on the outbreak of the Second World War. Of course it would have presented no problems in tracing the style, or rather the idea, of SF art back much earlier with the inclusion of artists like Bosch, Martin, or Durer, but as such artists are more than adequately represented elsewhere the space might better be devoted to those whose work is less well known, artists like Grandville and Albert Robida. The development and variety of SF art in the thirty years since 1940 has been so great that it could hardly even be hinted at in a volume this size which also deals with the formative years, rather it becomes a second work.

Like God or Kafka's Castle, the future is a great unknown which serves to mirror our desires, ambitions, fears, pre-occupations. Nowhere is this quite so readily apparent than in SF illustrations. If, as the truism has it, the future can only be interpreted in terms of the present, that present, *our* present, is viewed as cause for little optimism. Hopefully SF takes this pessimistic line so that it might serve more forcefully as a corrective to our gadarene technologies. An emetic, if you like, to what could develop once we start seeing the hardware of progress as a reward in itself, and a reckoning of its cost purely in terms of raw materials. Hopefully…

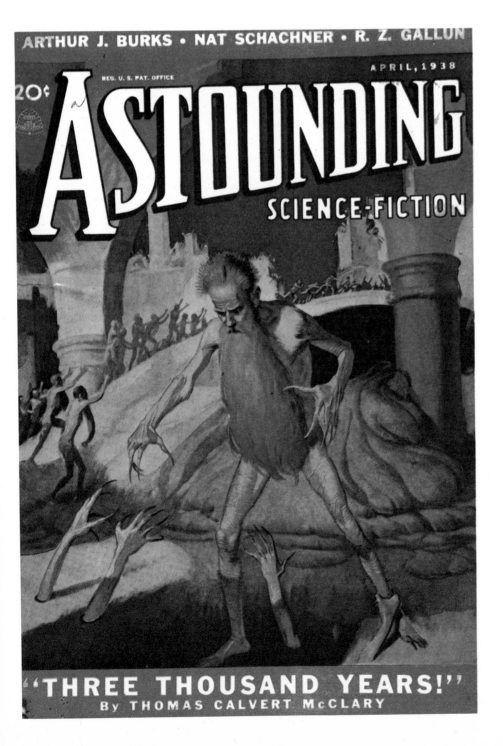

Howard V. Brown's cover illustration for Thomas Calvert McClary's 'Three Thousand Years', *Astounding*, April 1938.
Brown was one of the few illustrators to seriously challenge Paul's pre-eminence. His technique generally was more polished and his handling of colour more restrained and thoughtful.
The background figures are economically rendered and, combined with the grasping hands emerging from the ground, capture that intangible unease of a near-nightmare.

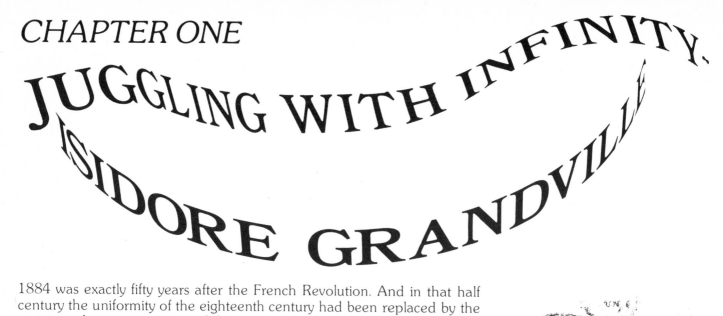

CHAPTER ONE
JUGGLING WITH INFINITY.
ISIDORE GRANDVILLE

1884 was exactly fifty years after the French Revolution. And in that half century the uniformity of the eighteenth century had been replaced by the variety and experimentation of the nineteenth, the legacy of the Paris barricades of 1796. Progress was ceasing to be a question of the moral development of man, rather more a synonym for industrial expansion. Mammon plus raw materials equals the rise of civilisation, a new revised formulation for those who like to keep on their toes. The God of Production was being born in the foam of effluent on every murky stream throughout Europe that could drive a water mill, supply a boiler, cool a furnace. This is the history we recognise! The precedents, the tradition, the justification even, so we tell ourselves, for whatever lamentable situation now befalls us!

1844 was a fine year in many ways: J. M. W. Turner's painting 'Rain, Steam and Speed' had been unveiled to cries of incredulity and disbelief – a prime example of Edgar Varése's observation that it is not the artist who is ahead of his time, but the people who are behind their's – for what more graphic epitaph could the birth of the Industrial Age have than this? Who can forget that uncertain form emerging from the mist, like some unspeakable archetype, a spectre of man-made energy battling the elements, a haunting reminder of the first machine age when expectation was all? What would eventually arise from the lurking fog?

1844 was also graced with the publication of several novels (remember that literary convention?) which are still avidly read today – Charles Dickens' *Martin Chuzzlewit*, Dumas' *The Three Musketeers*, and Eugene Sue's defiant and monstrous trio of volumes, *The Wandering Jew* (correction: two are avidly read, the third is avidly attempted).

1844 was the year laughing-gas (nitrous oxide) began to gain a widespread acceptance, though as a novelty more than anything else, its medical application was to come much later, and the year that Grassmann formulated his fourth-dimensional geometry. Fittingly perhaps, it was also the year that saw the publication of a remarkable volume of illustrations, the like of which had never been attempted before or since with such wild consumate artistry and originality, the work of a forty one year old Frenchman named Jean-Ignace-Isidore Gérard. The book was titled *Un Autre Monde* and all the engravings were executed by Gérard under his professional name of Grandville; he had also written the accompanying story under another pseudonym, Taxile Delord (from whence that practical joker of the 1880s, Leo Taxil?). Justly, *Un Autre Monde* was published by the foremost Paris printing and typographical house of the day, Fournier, in a strikingly modern looking edition.

An idea of the book's flavour and spirit can be obtained from the subtitle. It reads in full:

TRANSFORMATIONS, VISIONS, INCARNATIONS,
ASCENSIONS, LOCOMOTIONS, EXPLORATIONS,
PÉRÉGRINATIONS, EXCURSIONS, STATIONS.
COSMOGONIES, FANTASMAGORIES, REVERIES,
FOLATRERIES, FACÉTIES, LUBIES.
MÉTAMORPHOSES, ZOOMORPHOSES,
LITHOMORPHOSES, MÉTEMPSYCOSES, APOTHÉOSES,
ET AUTRE CHOSES.

Yet this is only a sampling! The staggering collection jumps from one

The assertive title page device for *Un Autre Monde*.

End device for the final chapter of *Un Autre Monde*.

marvellous conception to another, with scarcely a pause for breath. Almost every one of the volume's 294 pages features an illustration, each one seemingly more humorous, or bizarre, or pointed, or unnerving than the last. An extravaganza of satire and fantasy. One comes away gasping at the range and invention shown throughout every chapter!

Un Autre Monde was not the first collection to be published by Grandville. He had earlier illustrated *Gulliver's Travels*, and La Fontaine's *Fables*, both in 1838. The former, a particularly noteworthy edition, containing what must be his single most famous cut, the leather boot stamping on a crucifix. Grandville had also collaborated with his fellow artists, Daumier and Gavarni, on the illustrations for *Le Français peints par eux-mêmes* in 1840 (this was the volume that started the craze for *physiologie*, a particularly French type of book which explores the various human types, always with humour, often with satire). He had also produced a considerable number of lithographs, and jobbed on various illustrated periodicals of the time, this latter period obviously fitting him out with the accomplishments of speed and variety.

Grandville was born in Nancy in 1803, he had married the year before the publication of *Un Autre Monde*, and was dead three years after as a result of a weakened system ensuing from nervous depression. While he was much esteemed in France for his considerable body of work by 1844, the publication of *Un Autre Monde* did not seem to have had the impact one would have expected. It was, to borrow the phraseology of *Variety*, a flop-*d'estime*. Ironically, his greatest volume in terms of the public's acceptance, and the volume upon which his reputation rested throughout the Victorian period and onwards to the twentieth century, is *Les Fleurs Animées* which was published in the year of his death, 1847. What adds to this irony is that the last work, though perfectly befitting the sensibilities of the period, and therein the reason, is the one that holds much less interest today. Devoted as it is to finely rendered flowers with human faces dancing and cavorting in pastoral settings, *Les Fleurs Animées* seems a little too twee, pretty, sentimental.

Un Autre Monde may then have been another example of the public being behind the times, for it certainly hits a twentieth century nerve with its intense vision, its curious humour, its preoccupations. What then is Grandville's importance in the evolution of SF illustration? In terms of influence, none. There is no evidence that his work was a major inspiration and influence to anyone who could, no matter how remotely, be dubbed an SF artist. His importance resides in the fact that his work represents the culmination of many disparate elements of nineteenth century fantasy and reverie, that his vision is the culmination of a pre-technological approach to the universe, that his themes and concerns, as any cursory look through the following pages will show, are ones that he would share with the writers and artists of SF one hundred years later. To claim Grandville as an SF artist would be to do a diservice to both causes, yet none of the following illustrations would look out of place in the pages of *Amazing*, or *Astounding*, particularly in their earlier years, and the only jarring would be a matter of form, certainly not of content. Grandville's piercing eye deserves a place in any anthology of futurate art, we warm to that unique view of the universe.

Grandville, as has been noted, had little influence. His talent was too wild, too idiosyncratic, too rare. Some trace can be seen in the lithographs of Odilon Redon, very infrequently in the engravings of Doré, and who else? (Mention of Doré invites comparison between the two. Doré rarely matched the technique of Grandville, preferring generally a more blurred approach lacking the fine and exquisite detail characterised by the older artist. Doré's conceptions of content were anecdotal and heavily sentimental, he lacked the eye of Grandville for that little nuance of behaviour in humans, and in animals, which make the latter's work so much more convincing. Grandville was happy working within the medium he chose. Doré was not, he aspired to much grander designs, he wanted to paint epic religious canvases that would bludgeon the spectator into submission. Grandville was quite content with taking the visitor into his confidence. Therein the difference).

In the twentieth century, apart from an abortive revival at the hands of Andre Breton's Surrealists, and apart from those occasional space fillers in the *New York Review of Books* (aptly adjacent to the caricatures of David Levine), the work of Grandville is not very well know. Eclipsed by the ubiquitous Doré.

All the illustrations on the following pages are taken from *Un Autre Monde*. Only a small sample from a rich volume...

Grandville's Grandville. A finely executed self-portrait showing the artist at the age of thirty-six; sprightly eyes ready to depict the face behind the mask and compare the vanity of a coquette with that of a cockroach.

The militia of *Un Autre Monde* being ordered into battle by the Napoleonic supremo.

The Infinity Juggler. The world as Court Jester's whim and conceit. Earths fall through the ether as man looks on alarmed and impotent, terrified yet concerned. Grandville's *Weltenschauung?* Possibly. The bitter-sweet vision of a manic-depressive. Comedy edging over into tragedy in some far off corner of the cosmos. If Grandville had ever decided upon a trademark this would be it.

The menagerie of hybrids and grotesques. The legacy of Dr Moreau has become a public display, like the lunatics of Bedlam. This mixing of animals was common in much of Grandville's work, it was a theme he returned to again and again. With an eye on the terminology of the day hé has called these creatures *les doublivores!*

(LEFT) A crustacean trio, soon to be joined by five beetles, dance in the centre, flanked on the one side by grasshoppers, on the other by rats. A suggestion of menace, typical in Grandville's work, creeps in when one realises that these beetles are carrying hammers! The willing suspension of disbelief here is quite remarkable. Evidence of the artist's acute eye in capturing the mannerisms of animals. Walt Disney's *Fantasia* was never quite like this.

(RIGHT) Transformations at the human menagerie. The women look so essentially nineteenth century here, facially that is, quite apart from their costume. Who is the birdlike figure to the rear? What designs does the man with one arm have?

(BELOW) Hybrids again, produced by the cosmic vivisector. A childhood reverie manifested. What would happen if...? One hundred years ago such creations were produced 'out of the air.' Today an elaborate scientific rationale, complete with easy to follow instructions, would be given.

(TOP LEFT) Balancing across the pit of un-speakables, the tightrope walkers make their way precariously toward a harem of beauties. Notice particularly in the pit, the pair of un-supported serrated-edge scissors, blending in so well with the other creatures. Grandville's dexterity in investing life in the non-animate is disturbing.

(LOWER LEFT) The classical looking beauty merely dips her foot in the pool of the enchained dog-man as the water-carrier(?) offers a goblet to her. People as property?

(ABOVE) The Carrot Brigand stands defiantly, the blood of two onions is on his hands. Is this the secret life of plants (and vedge)? The carrot is an ugly and frightful creation, the gentle onions elicit our sympathy. Here is the night-kitchen, and Grandville convinces us that this is a regular occurence.

(BELOW) More *doublivores!* This time on a Saturday evening at their Sports and Social Club! A fine chandelier composed of geo-metrical shapes hangs like Damocles' sword over the heads of the dancers. The snake on the stairs is rather startled to see someone here she did not expect. A fish mask on the floor serves to remind us of the illusion.

(LEFT) One of His fingers? Yes, *le Doight de Dieu.* Subtitled, *Pour la critique impartiale,* Grandville, or rather the mellifluously named Taxile Delord, assures us that this creation surpasses the finest masterpieces of antiquity. A work of genius produced quite objectively, without the prejudices of a mere human. What appears to be the head of the sculptor is in fact a hammer he is holding in his right hand.

(BELOW) As a spectre of the future this compares favourably with some of Albert Robida's illustrations to be seen in the next chapter. A fantasmagoria of the future, stamping out life as it proceeds, inexorably. In its left hand it holds a serpent and scales, in its right, a broomstick and an ear-trumpet! Is progress a little hard in hearing what we shout to it about the future? On the ground, on the back of an upturned canvas, the date 1943, the year of Auschwitz at its maximum capacity.

The anthropomorphic heavens…
(LEFT) The canopy of the clouds is pulled back to reveal Miss Moon arising from bed, while Mr Sun retires for the night. An evocative and playful representation of an archetypal image, conjuring up for us lost thoughts, childhood imaginings.
(RIGHT) Another variation on the same theme. The lantern of the night is extinguished for another night. The Big Curtain is being lowered. Here there be dreams… The Night Thoughts of Grandville, expressing perhaps, the view of the world as a whimsical charade, the secret of which continually eludes us.

(RIGHT) The star as an ear-ring of a woman gazing dreamily across the cosmos. The lights in the heavens as the gee-gaws of higher beings.

(BELOW, LEFT AND RIGHT) Grandville returns to a favourite occupation, the instilling of life in the inanimate. Without so much as changing a single feature in the telescopes and dividers they become remarkably human-like as they bear mute witness to an eclipse, here depicted as a kiss. Cybernated instruments with a purpose beyond the wildest dreams of their creators.

(BELOW) The twilight world of the roof-tops. Weather-vanes, lightening-conductors, and other forms which haunt these regions just above our heads. The foreground figure, complete with pipe, nonchalantly directs a streak of lightening into a pail from which emerges a cloud with a face, angry with the circumstances.

Grandville would have been no stranger to machines like computers which can operate and make decisions without continual human intervention. Is the difference between a ratchet and a memory-bank quantative or qualitative?

(LEFT) Playthings from the human toyshop? M. C. Escher has remarked on the wheel not occuring in nature and has attempted to devise a creature which could plausibly utilise the form, quite successfully. But what about the inverted dome? Could this have been as viable? Organic skittles pivoting on a concentrated mass of bone? What course would such an evolution have taken? Could intelligence develop without the purposeful locomotion of limbs? Grandville proffers a suggestion...

(RIGHT) Mechanical puppets mock their creators. Programmed for the dance, they eagerly seek our approval with searching smiles on the completion of their routine.

(BELOW) Like a galactic Willow Pattern, the Bridge of Infinities spans the Solar System in four arches. The Space Pilgrim is taking a stroll over the ether towards Saturn which, girded as it is by a balcony, seems to be one of the very places to visit. In the distance is a small hut, atop which a flag flutters in the space winds, where refreshment may be had. These are good examples of Grandville's childlike reverie, credible extravaganza spiced with curious humour. We experience a constant sense of *de ja-vu.* Everything looks so familiar, where have we seen them before?

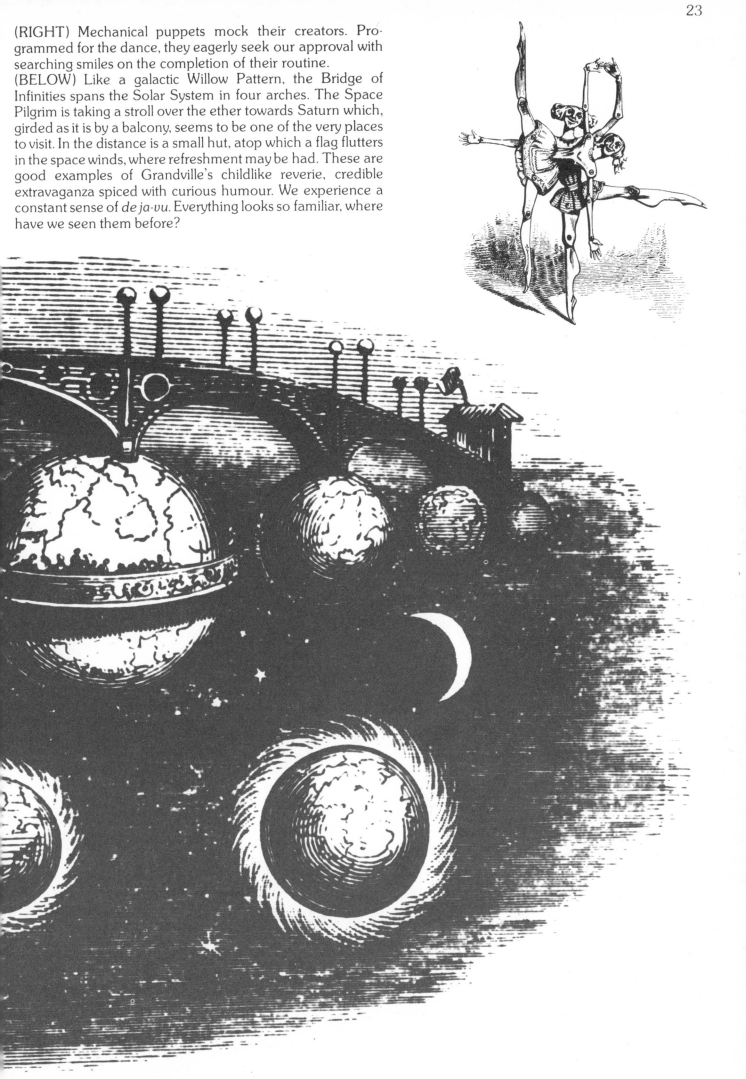

(LEFT) *Plantes Marines, Coquillages, Madrepores.* Clusters of dice and crosses have sprouted and grown like the rare rock plants of a distant landscape. Egyptian obelisks, decorated with hieroglyphics, have begun to duplicate themselves taking their cue from a colony of pyramids who always do so well in this type of soil. Dominoes and crystal forms are also very much in evidence. A nightmare of geometries on the Planet of Against-Nature.

(BELOW) *La Bataille des Cartes.* The card game reaches its ultimate conclusion with the slaughter of the packs. A heart pierced by a club, a fragile wall of kings, queens, and jacks, the pips battling it out. To the fore, epitomes of the four suits.

(RIGHT) This disturbing metamorphosis assaults us with its incongrous imagery. A surrealist rebus perhaps, containing the secrets of the universe? A figure with root-like hair is being clubbed at the beginning, at the end another figure is about to be consumed by horrendous fish. In between, eyes, horsemen, suggestions of the Church of Rome, a column torn asunder, pointing and plaintive hands. What are we to make of it?

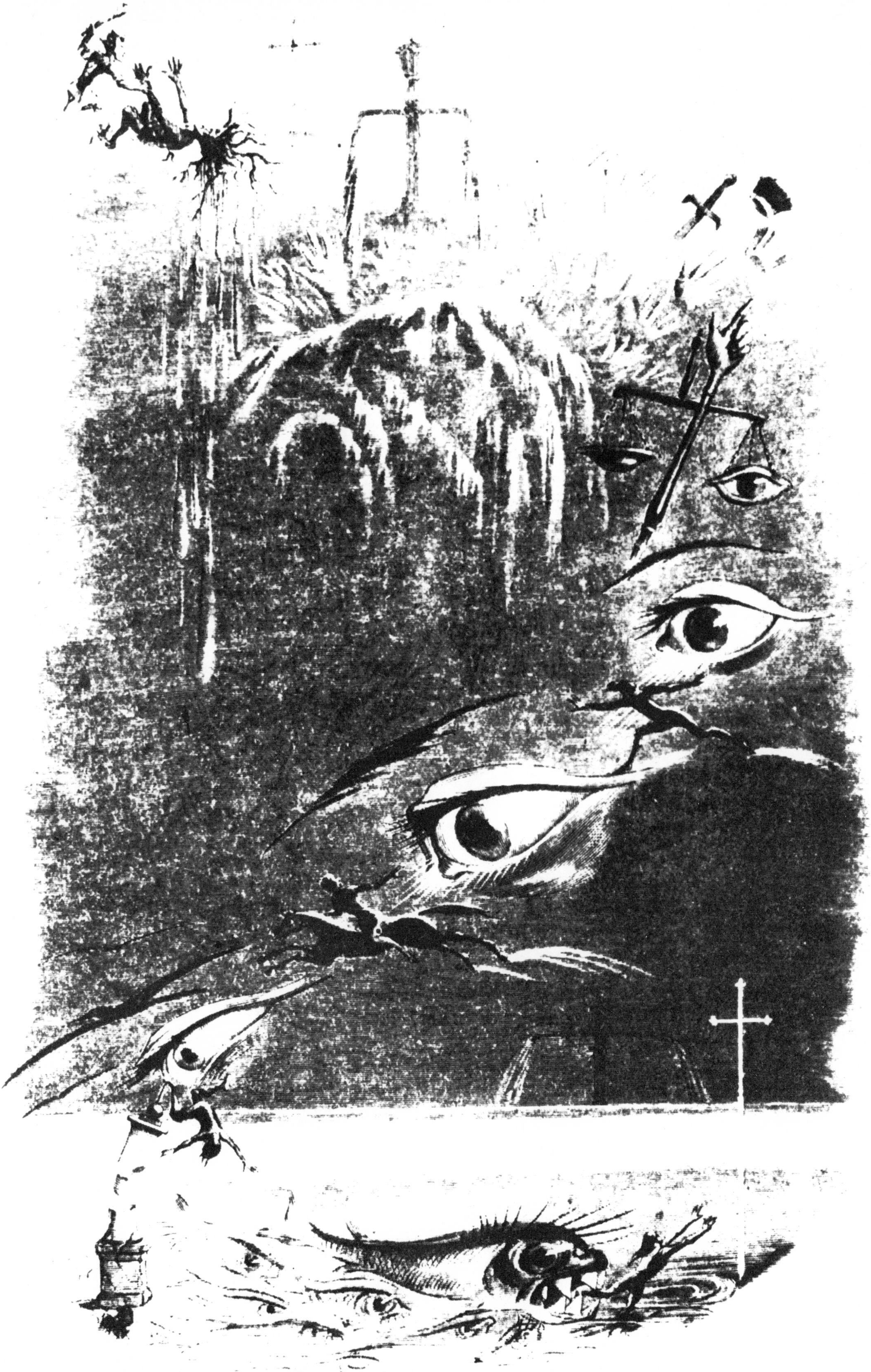

(LEFT) The Constitution is irremovable (for the time being, that is) in the face of the high and low, the new order and the status quo. Significantly the populace is protrayed as a steam driven ship, the opposition merely as a lobster. The scales are tipped on the side of the greatest number, the side with technology on its mind. This is the direction progress will take.

(BELOW) Cosmic joksters. Are we nothing more than bubbles blown by the gods in their idle moments? Bubbles they can prick on a whim? It would be tempting to see this, and certain earlier illustrations as evidence of Grandville's depressive condition. The tragic sense of life.

(ABOVE) A highly original form of loco-motion! And an expeditious one at that! Extrapolation; it is merely a question of taking an existing device and enlarging it sufficiently to accomplish the task at hand. The question which staggers us is who, or what, is on the end?

(LEFT) More *doublivores*, on a land-scape straight out of Max Ernst. The dog-tortoise, the snake-bear, and the pelican-insect are simple composites with each part readily identifiable. The man-horse though, the rider, is a subtle blending of the two, each part merging almost imperceptively into the other.

✧　　✧　　✧

This selection of the work of Isidore Grandville shows us the state of fantastic art in the mid-nineteenth century. We have seen these illustrations as a cul-mination of the pre-technological approach. We have seen how the artist, through the depiction of such devices as telescopes and dividers, was flirting with a more machinistic subject matter. The great advances of science, spawned by the Industrial Revolution, would give a firmer base to such strivings. It was only a matter of time before someone would grasp these great potentialities…

CHAPTER TWO
FROLICS IN THE FUTURE~ ALBERT ROBIDA

One of the most popular book and journal illustrators in the latter half of the nineteenth century in France was the painter and lithographer Albert Robida (1848-1926). He was a prolific worker and examples of his sketching and drawing were to be seen regularly in almost every magazine and review of the day. His editions of Rabelais and Villon were justly praised, notably the former in two great volumes with sumptuous pictorial gilt bindings, while his long series of works depicting the architecture, life, and customs of Paris through the ages served not only to enhance further his reputation but also to ensure the preservation of many of the buildings to which he had directed attention.

In 1880 Robida began an association with the popular humorous periodical *La Caricature* which lasted through until 1886. As an artist of repute, much in the manner of a present day columnist, he was given a free hand to do as he pleased. He immediately launched into the writing of a long series describing the fortune and misfortune of several families in the future, a sort of *Forsyth Saga* set in the France of the mid-twentieth century, which came to be the first sustained vision of futuristic war technology that had yet been created. The series proved immensely popular, an indication of the Victorians' changing regard to science, and was soon collected into several volumes that were published throughout the 1880s under the general title of *Le Vingtième Siècle*.

The work was richly illustrated and, as I. F. Clarke remarks (*Voices Prophesying War: 1763-1984*, London 1966, p. 93), it is these illustrations — certainly not the light-weight text — which permit a favourable comparison of Robida with his contemporary across the English Channel, H. G. Wells.

The world of the 1950s presented by the artist was merely the Victorian society of his day with the addition of technological marvels like television, rapid-transit systems, submarines, etc. These innovations did not in any way change the assumptions, conventions, and structure of that society; they might simply have been tacked on as an afterthought. Of course, people could travel from Paris to Madrid in little over an hour, be shelled with typhoid canisters by an enemy several hundred miles away, use the public video-phone to talk to their friends on the other side of the world, but that was the end of it! Robida, like his contemporaries, could not picture the ramifications of these developments. Nevertheless, his accomplishment in depicting the great potentiality of science, notably in the way that it would alter the conduct of war, cannot be over emphasised (see again I. F. Clarke, *op. cit.*, p. 90 *et seq.* who has much of importance to say about Robida. Clarke's study cannot be recommended too highly. It does what every history of SF patently fails to do — relate the literature to contemporary psychology and events).

The pencil and crayon drawings reproduced here have a deftness and humour which is characteristic of all of Robida's work, whether futuristic or not. Even something so appalling as the casualtys of chemical and bacteriological warfare (called by the artist, *la guerre miasmatique*) manages to convey an impression of lightness and distancing. This feeling is added to in the way the great inventions seem to overpower the people. These frail humans look somehow out of place, dwarfed by the achievement around them. The fruits of progress seem not to belong to them, to be part of another tradition. Perhaps it is just a coincidence that such a view would become increasingly more apparent in the real world over the ensuing decades. Its

Albert Robida — Victorian paterfamilias and creator of the first sustained vision of future war technologies. A self-portrait.

Electricity straddles the world. Title design for Chapter One of *La Vie Électrique*.

LE VINGTIÉME SIÈCLE
La Vie électrique

culmination would be reached in the First World War when the foot-slogging ranks would be offered up for sacrifice as the Germans justified their use of gas by waving a copy of Robida's *La Guerre au Vingtième Siècle* (1887) and shouting, 'But it was your idea! Not our's!'

Robida, then, may be considered the first modern science fiction artist even though his vision was still nineteenth century in its structure. He projected the science of his day far ahead and was sufficiently philosophic to regard what he saw with detachment. His sojourn in the days to be threw other contemporary projections into sharp relief and shamed them for their lack of perspective. The storehouse of the future was replenished and, like his descendants working in the same vein fifty years later, the world he placed there had very little to recommend. it.

The idea that the future-as-history serves as a corrective has already been mentioned. Yet the more one studies the visions of the period since the Industrial Revolution, the more it becomes apparent that they are ones of death, destruction, alienation. Is it a conceit to see SF as having this function? All the following illustrations are taken from two volumes in Robida's series. These are the first volume which bore the title the whole series would be known as, *Le Vingtième Siècle* (1883), and a later work, dating from circa 1887, *La Vie Électrique*. Neither books have ever been published outside of France and it is hoped that their inclusion here will prompt further examination of the artist and his work.

The energy explosion. Electricity liberates and enslaves the world — personified as a provocative woman with evil intent (and an Elsa Lanchester hairdo). Overall, very reminiscent of Ernst Fuchs.

(RIGHT) Robida, as has been noted, termed chemical warfare, *la guerre miasmatique*, and it was a tactic much favoured by the inhabitants of the artist's mid-twentieth century world.

Here casualties are administered an antidote by a medical officer in a gas mask. The chemical big gun on the battlements is disturbingly convincing in its design.

(LEFT) *Corps Medical Offensif.* Howitzer-like canon propel shells containing typhus and other deadly 'miasmas' into the enemy trenches. Warfare has reached a new level of sophistication. 'We will enlist the support of the microbes in our just cause', proclaims an Important Person. This is one side of the reality, a sneak preview of the Great War.

(RIGHT) *Les mitrailleurs.* Tactical machine-gunners from the Chemical Corps. Bacteriological snipers picking off the enemy with a couple of well places cc's of a deadly fluid.

(RIGHT) A march past by the members of the 8th Chemical Company. The carriage gun, impressive as it is, is not characteristic of Robida's work. He usually preferred more restrained conceptions.

The horses here, like the soldiers, were provided with gas masks and carried air-tanks on their backs.

From the gun emplacements of the front line the intrepid war correspondent telephones news of the latest developments back to Paris. (Does the land-line suggest 'live-coverage' for those unfortunate enough not to be present?).

Modern war reporting had scarcely existed for more than thirty years in 1883. It had begun with William Russell's despatches from the Crimea in 1854-56, and its importance would rise with every war, conflict, and skirmish throughout the second half of the nineteenth

century. Here Robida underscores its role as Everyman's friend with a ring-side seat at the Spectacle of Our Times. The confusion and destruction, the suspended clouds of smoke overshadowing the battlefield like a shroud, the menace in the trim features of the guns, are like a premonition of the Great War. The Great War when technology outstripped the human imagination.

(ABOVE) *Les donjons flottants.* The ultimate in naval design — vast near-impregnable floating fortresses. Marine redoubts. Extravaganzas of steel plating and rivets!

The French navy had introduced its first ironclads in 1858 and Robida had sensed that it would not be long before they would take on the appearance of the castle and blockhouse. He was right. The apogee of the ironclad was how he had pictured it — in principal, if not in design.

(BELOW LEFT) *Les donjons flottants (de poche?).* A smaller tactical battleship engaged in action at the siege of Buenos Aires. Gun turrets, occupying every available position, contrast oddly with the two masts, relics of (or salutes to?) a now bygone age.

The artillery smoke and evening clouds conspire to present another premonition of the Great War. It might almost be a photo-engraving from a contemporary issue of the *Daily Graphic* celebrating a near-forgotten skirmish off Heligoland (or wherever).

(BELOW) *Les grandes chasses sous-marines.* Robida acknowledges Jules Verne's Captain Nemo *(20,000 Leagues Under the Sea)* who had made his debut some thirteen years earlier in 1870.

(ABOVE) The *Ville de Bordeux*, a passenger vessel which sails on the surface in good weather and heads down to thirty fathoms at the slightest sign of a storm. The new technology is available to all, including the ubiquitous holidaymakers.

(RIGHT) A convoy of submarines. The smaller craft nestle under the mother ship prior to a surprise raid on the port of Brest.

(BELOW) *Les torpédistes.* An advance submarine is discovered by frogman-scouts jetting about on one-man craft.

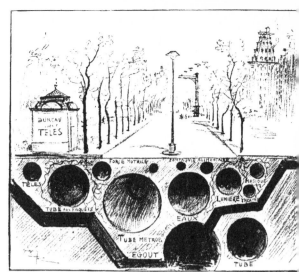

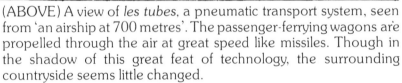

(ABOVE) A view of *les tubes*, a pneumatic transport system, seen from 'an airship at 700 metres'. The passenger-ferrying wagons are propelled through the air at great speed like missiles. Though in the shadow of this great feat of technology, the surrounding countryside seems little changed.

(ABOVE, TOP) A cross section of underground Paris showing, in addition to *les tubes*, the tunnels constructed for the various public utilities such as sewerage disposal, drinking water, electricity, and, surprisingly, television (termed *le télé* by Robida!).
(ABOVE, CENTRE AND LOWER) *Les tubes*. The inside of a *wagon* showing its comfortable padded upholstery. And below, the *Paris Express*, one such *wagon*, prior to departure.
(LEFT) Off for a cheap weekend in Spain! Passengers boarding the *Madrid Express* at the *Gare du Sud*, one of the principal termini of *les tubes* in Paris. Notice the wind recorders which, in this context, *seem positively quaint.*

(ABOVE, LEFT TO RIGHT) *Les aerocabs.* The aeronautical taxi-cabs which will ferry you back and forth across Paris should you tire of *les tubes* come in two distinct types, *les balloons* and *les pneumatiques.* In the centre we see a tower at Saint-Jacques which has been put to secular use, as a cab-rank.

(LEFT) Fledgling air-traffic control. A lighthouse, or danger beacon, warns the aeronauts of a treacherous range of high mountains. Decrease altitude immediately!

(RIGHT) A small country house with the very latest in exterior decor — an ascending *pavillon*, or summerhouse. Had William Randolph Hearst only seen this illustration when he was planning Saint Simeon!

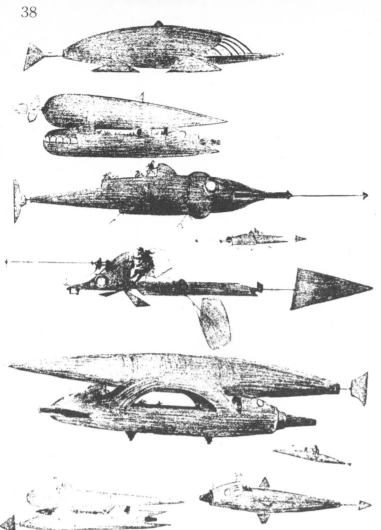

(ABOVE) A large packet-ship advances across the west of Paris, against a rapidly changing skyline. A flotilla of smaller craft has been sent to investigate.

(LEFT) A selection of mid-twentieth century airships, available to emergent nation and wealthy individual alike. Most of them have a design which betrays their nautical origin.

(BELOW) Tourists aboard a pleasure craft take in a period castle.

(ABOVE) Trouble at twelve thousand feet aboard a two-man craft. Safety precautions seem minimal.

(BELOW) An army scout, in communication with ground base via a long cable, reports sightings in the far off hills. This craft is termed a *hélicoptère* by Robida.

(RIGHT) *Nos fleuves et notre atmosphère.* A telling depiction of a world gagging in its own waste. A vindicated image of pollution.

(LEFT) The Socialist Experiment of 1922 and what happened to it! Albert Robida was not greatly impressed with the work of Karl Marx.

(RIGHT) The Sphinx in a cold climate. Weather engineering became a priority in Robida's world of the future and the reclaiming of the Sahara regions for agriculture was a notable early success. The pavillion-styled buildings became as widely spread as Hilton Hotels, not even the Great Pyramid could evade them for long. An earth restyled…

(ABOVE) *Telephonoscopique* kiosks are to be found on every street-corner in the better neighbourhoods throughout France in the mid-twentieth century. Not only can you speak with your distant friends and loved ones in all the corners of the Empire, you can also see them at the same time. An intriguing forecast and aptly titled *le télé*.

(ABOVE) Frustrated and enraged at obtaining so many crossed visual lines, a man hurls a chair at *le télé*. An observation by Robida that while tremendous strides may be made in technology, human behaviour changes not in the slightest.

(LEFT) Treatment for the physically exhausted in an incubator-like device *(la couveuse)* which rejuvenates the mind as well as the body.

(RIGHT) A public telephone *sans le télé*. This is the model which is found on every street-corner. The drinking fountain, with matching trough for dogs, is an apotheosis of late nineteenth century sensibility.

(BELOW, LEFT) A crack battalion of women arrives to defend the barricades during the revolution of 1953. While they may be engaging in what hitherto has been considered a male preserve, their costume remains distinctly feminine.

The Old World is swept away by the advance of tech-nology and its siblings – Progress. The cherished history and traditions of a bygone age are carted-off or dynamited. The 'old deal', pictured as a winged angel, will be banished to a museum *avec autres curiosités.* The background figure to the right, presiding over the cultural carnage, with its retort head, its shoulders of cog wheels, its arms supporting an electric light and a mason's rule, is a disturbing spectre. A per-sonification of the new regime. Albert Robida's frolics in the future were over, the warning would now be given. This is the real cost of the Paris air-cabs, *les tubes, le télé,* and other novelties. Technology does not exist in a vacuum. It percolates through every level and area of society. *You will only know the true price when it is too late!*

CHAPTER THREE

BY PULLMAN CAR TO VENUS ~ VICTORIANS... AND OTHERS!

After the world of Albert Robida this chapter might almost be considered an interlude, reflecting as it does the more popular and less committed work of artists from other traditions. This selection can be regarded as representative of the late nineteenth century, and continues the story onwards until the outbreak of the First World War. There are several examples which pre-date Robida and some which are contemporary with him. It will be noted that little attention was paid to his innovations.

While the works of H. G. Wells and Jules Verne were vitally important in the evolution of SF *writing*, their illustrators largely reflected the formal conventions of an earlier period and added little that was new to the vocabulary of futurate art.

To the Victorians accomplishment and achievement were everything, and science, which had obviously created so much, was uniformly regarded as one of His prime blessings. This is readily apparent in the following pages, yet at the same time there is an undertone which hints that all may not be quite as we expect it to be. Murmourings questioning the enshrined idol. From this middle period it is the work of Warwick Goble for Wells' *The War of the Worlds* which stands out as having an intensity and immediacy which would come to characterise the work of the twentieth century.

After the turn of the century, when the spectre of the coming war loomed ahead almost as a death wish of the collective unconscious, certain American illustrators were evolving a style which had made a break with the earlier whimsy and was rooted in hard political realities (from whence their inspiration). These artists reflected the heightened state of future-consciousness which had been so great a force in the shaping of the New World (pps. 50-51). The progress of science was proceeding ahead at a steady pace and soon it would vault away leaving mankind as perplexed as a rat in a laboratory maze. Then what?...

Two engravings by Gustav Doré which may be considered representative of his approach to the fantastic, i.e. interesting but lacking any conviction. On the left, the galleon transporting *Baron Munchausen* to the Moon, and, to the right, a breathtaking view of the Devil descending to Earth from *The Bible*.

(RIGHT) As has been noted, the French navy had introduced the first iron-clads in 1858. It was not until four years later, in 1862, that the British navy followed suit. This *Punch* prediction of 'A Tar of the Future' dates from that year and reflects the increasing importance iron-plating would have in the evolution of warfare.

(ABOVE LEFT, LEFT & RIGHT) Three imaginative engravings executed by Hildibrand for Jules Verne's prescient novel, *From the Earth to the Moon*, published in 1865. The lunar voyage described by Verne was the first to be based on sound scientific principles (initially anyway) as opposed to the more usual mere magical hocu-pocus. The Gun Club of Baltimore, an organisation uniquely American, simply built an enormous canon that would fire the projectile and its occupants straight to the Moon. The fact that the space-gun was located in Tampa, Florida, not a hundred miles from Cape Kennedy, is a startling coincidence. Verne had perceived the increasingly important role the New World would assume in future technology. The engraving, above left, showing the effects of weightlessness upon the pioneer cosmonauts, is one of SF's most famous illustrations.

Further illustrations from Verne's *From the Earth to the Moon.*

(ABOVE LEFT) The space travellers seem to have very little difficulty in breathing on the Moon! The terrain still appears convincing to us today, capturing as it does the desolateness of the surface.

(ABOVE TOP RIGHT) The influence of Grandville? Yes, but less playful and more violent.

(ABOVE RIGHT) The projectile in full flight. Hurtling (or should it be *chugging*?) towards its destination as Queen Victoria, one would like to think, searches the heavens through her spy-glass in agitated expectation.

(LEFT) Return to Earth – splashdown, another prescient Vernian touch. Note the American flag above the module.

Three engravings from a later work of Jules Verne's, *Robur le Conquérant*, translated as The Clipper of the Clouds, dating from 1886 — the year of Robert Louis Stevenson's *Dr. Jekyll and Mr. Hyde*.

The hero of the story is Robur, a shadowy figure with unlimited wealth who builds a giant airship, or *aeronef*, which leads him into many adventures around the world. Verne was hesitant in putting his future marvels of science into military service, and one of the very few occasions when he did occurs in the present book as Robur rescues the intended victims of a sacrifice by firing on the inhabitants of Dahomey. Generally Verne's technology existed in a vacuum, it had little social consequences. A major difference between him and the modern SF writers (See I. F. Clarke, *Voices Prophesying War 1763-1984*, London 1966, for a most perceptive analysis of Verne's work in this context).

(ABOVE LEFT) The *aeronef* journeys gracefully through a range of mountains. Note the vast banks of vertical propellers, in addition to the fore and aft screws.

(ABOVE RIGHT) A closer view of the *aeronef* and one of its smaller sister ships — a tactical craft. The design of the mother ship is clearly maritime inspired.

(RIGHT) On the decks of the *aeronef* — a maintenance inspection?

(ABOVE) 'We perceived the cars of the Mercurians floating in space'. A superb fantasy by Paul Hardy for the *English Illustrated Magazine*, 1887, showing flotillas of Martian ships approaching a craft from Earth. The two English cosmonauts, without the benefit of either protective suits or oxygen supply, stand proudly on the tower of the ship musing on the Empire's expansion...

(LEFT) The inevitable result of the Railway Mania should it go unchecked. This is how the American review, *Judge,* saw turn-of-the-century New York in 1884. Everything subjugated to the Railway Interest!

(BELOW) One of the most notable (if that be the epithet) writers to emerge from the dime-novel school in America was Frank Reade, Jr., a pseudonym of Lu Senarens who, according to Brian Aldiss, produced some forty million words in thirty years. Fantastic marvels figured prominently in many of his works and there always seemed to be an artist around to match his vision. The uncredited illustration below is from *'The Boys of New York'*, 1892, and shows an airship with wings that flap—a proposition for powered flight that was seriously considered at the time.

(LEFT) Flying machines circling over the city of London. An illustration for the serialisation of 'The Abduction of Alexandra Seine', which appeared in the Harmsworth Magazine, London 1896. While less visually impressive than many of the imagined air vehicles of the day — the rocket noses, the construction of the encased propellers — are a credit to the anonymous illustrator.

(BELOW LEFT) Another masterly execution — an engraving by Fernand Fau for Le Faure's Les Robinson Lunaires (1893), showing the jettisoning of a module over the Moon. Note the anchor suspended from the main body.

(ABOVE AND BELOW) Three drawings by Fred T. Jane for E. Douglas Fawcett's Hartmann the Anarchist; Or, The Doom of a Great City, serialised in the English Illustrated Magazine, 1896. These giant ships, again built with the private capital of one man, are a reflection of the age's anxiety. In the American pulps of the 1920s and onwards the enemy was the malevolent extra-terrestrial. In the 1890s it was the anarchist or nihilist.

H. G. Wells' *The War of the Worlds* was originally serialised in *Pearson's Magazine* in 1897. It was the first of the author's works to be illustrated, and the artist, Warwick Goble, more than matched the Wellsian imagination in his paintings of the invasion by Martians.

(ABOVE) Two dramatic title headings by Goble which show a transition from the older formal approach to the modern near-abstract.

(BELOW) The Martians, encased inside their highly protective vehicles, smash through Surrey as the population flees.

(ABOVE) The Martians are finally vanquished, not by Man's belligerent technologies, but by bacteria. An invader, unprotected by its armour, dies on a grassy knoll somewhere in the Home Counties...

(BELOW) The Martians loose control of their vehicles as the microscopic organisms begin to wreak their effect. A drawing by Goble which ranks as one of the classic SF illustrations.

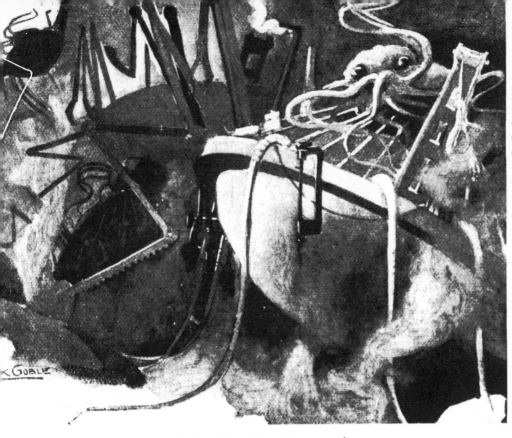

(LEFT) A Martian Handling Machine and its dying occupant, an octopus-like creature totally dependant on its hardware creations. Wells, in *The War of the Worlds*, bequeathed to us an extra-terrestial consciousness — we would never look at the night sky in quite such the same way.

Three illustrations from Wells' *The First Men in the Moon*, published in 1901. The unknown artist failed to match the standard set by Goble.
(BELOW) Bedford and Professor Cavor, the protagonists, are discovered by insect-like beings soon after their arrival on the Moon.
(BELOW RIGHT LOWER) Cavor is captured by the Selenites, strange distorted inhabitants of the Moon's interior.
(BELOW RIGHT UPPER) The craft which transports the two worthies to the Earth's satellite. It was made of 'Cavorite', a gravity defying material (a Wellsian lapse), and the overall design resembles a period vacuum cleaner.

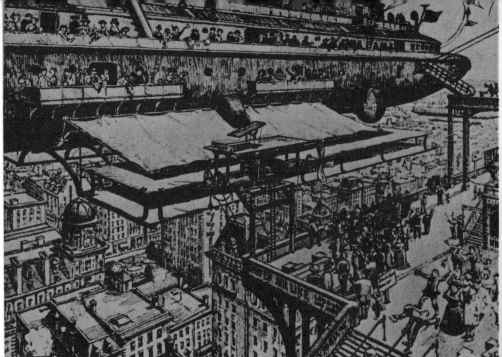

Three compelling examples of early twentieth century American futuristic illustration taken from contemporary magazines.

(ABOVE) A United Air Line terminal situated high atop a skyscraper above the streets of New York. The craft is an airship with propellers, then considered the only possible future for aviation. Artist unknown. *Life* magazine, 1910.

(LEFT) *Life's* view as to what would befall America should she not enter the Great War. An epic design by Harry Grant Dart guaranteed to feed the anti-German sentiments of 1917.

(BELOW) Aircraft of the future hovering above New York. The detail of the planes is hardly discernible yet this is more than compensated for by the vertigo-inducing perspective of the skyscrapers, a foretaste of things to come! Stylishly drawn by Bus, *Judge* magazine, 1911.

Gordon Grant's illustrations for Jack London's pessimistic tale of the future, *The Scarlet Plague* (1912), reflected the unease of an artist working within an alien tradition. Yet one sees an echo of this drawing, suggesting as it does a metaphor for a nuclear explosion, in several of the posters produced by the peace movement in the 1960s. A skull in the sky, a haunting image of the twentieth century's power of complete and absolute destruction.

CHAPTER FOUR

'The pterodactyl has gotten into the transformer!' ~AMAZING.

Hugo Gernsback (1884-1967) may not have been the 'Father of Science Fiction' as so often has been claimed, but that he made a substantial contribution to the development of the genre no one could deny. To say that he gave SF an almost universal popularity at the cost of castrating its literacy is not far from the truth.

Soon after Gernsback's arrival in the United States from Luxembourg in 1904 he was selling radio and phonograph equipment and spare parts, publishing the first radio magazine ever, *Modern Electrics*, and generally keeping his eye on the main chance, electro-scientific-mechanics*wise*. His great entrepreneurial energy and persistent brashness remind the present writer of the gangster in a Preston Sturges film who observes, in thick Brooklynese, 'America is the land of opportunity!' Gernsback was an archetypal New World success.

In 1911 *Modern Electrics* serialised a novel written by Gernsback which had the compelling title of *Ralph 124C 41+ ; A Romance of the Year 2660*. This Irish stew of words was warmly received, which says much for the public's appreciation of prose bereft of sensitivity, devoid of humour, pedestrian in the extreme, and evincing enthusiasm for nothing more than the most abject of gadgets. Similar stories by other hands appeared in the various Gernsback publications throughout the next fifteen years and, in April 1926, Gernsback launched the world's very first science fiction magazine, *Amazing Stories*; the tenor of the contributions had been established by *Ralph* — scientific pornography for the mechanically minded. Writing which drooled over descriptions of technology.

Gernsback lost control of *Amazing* in 1929 and immediately began a new magazine, *Science Wonder Stories* (see Chapter Seven), which was the mixture much as before.

The colour covers, in addition to the black and white interior illustrations, were executed by an artist who was to become the greatest single name in SF art — Frank R. Paul, a Gernsback discovery. Paul had little or no precedent from which to gain inspiration and it is a fitting tribute to his incredible imagination that his vision and stylisation of SF would characterise all similar work for the next forty years. Paul, when illustrating a story, created these monstrous galactic cities, alien landscapes, and mechanical Behemoths entirely himself — the descriptions contained in the stories were never ever much more specific than, for example, something like, 'shimmering towers rising into the clouds from a crystal-like terrain'. He had a bias for the epic conception and many of his best covers depict vast vistas with vanishing-point perspective which, nonetheless, still had a painstaking and elaborate attention to the smallest detail that one could equate with the work of John Martin.

Paul had studied to be an architect and his training is reflected in the formal geometry which graces his finest designs. When it came to extra-terrestial creatures and cosmic beings his work frequently lapsed into cliché-ridden forms that seldom escaped the comedic. Few of his BEMs appear as convincing and frightening as he had obviously wished, their appearance is friendly and domesticated almost. Similarly with his human figures, often with unjust proportions, and resembling more an early children's animated film.

To say that all of what follows in the present book is a testimony to Paul's unique creativity would not be hyperbole. No other individual enlarged so greatly the vocabulary of twentieth century popular art in its attempts at grasping the future...

The world of *Amazing!* Technological hi-jinks in the world of the day after tomorrow. Snapshots from a sojourn in the future.

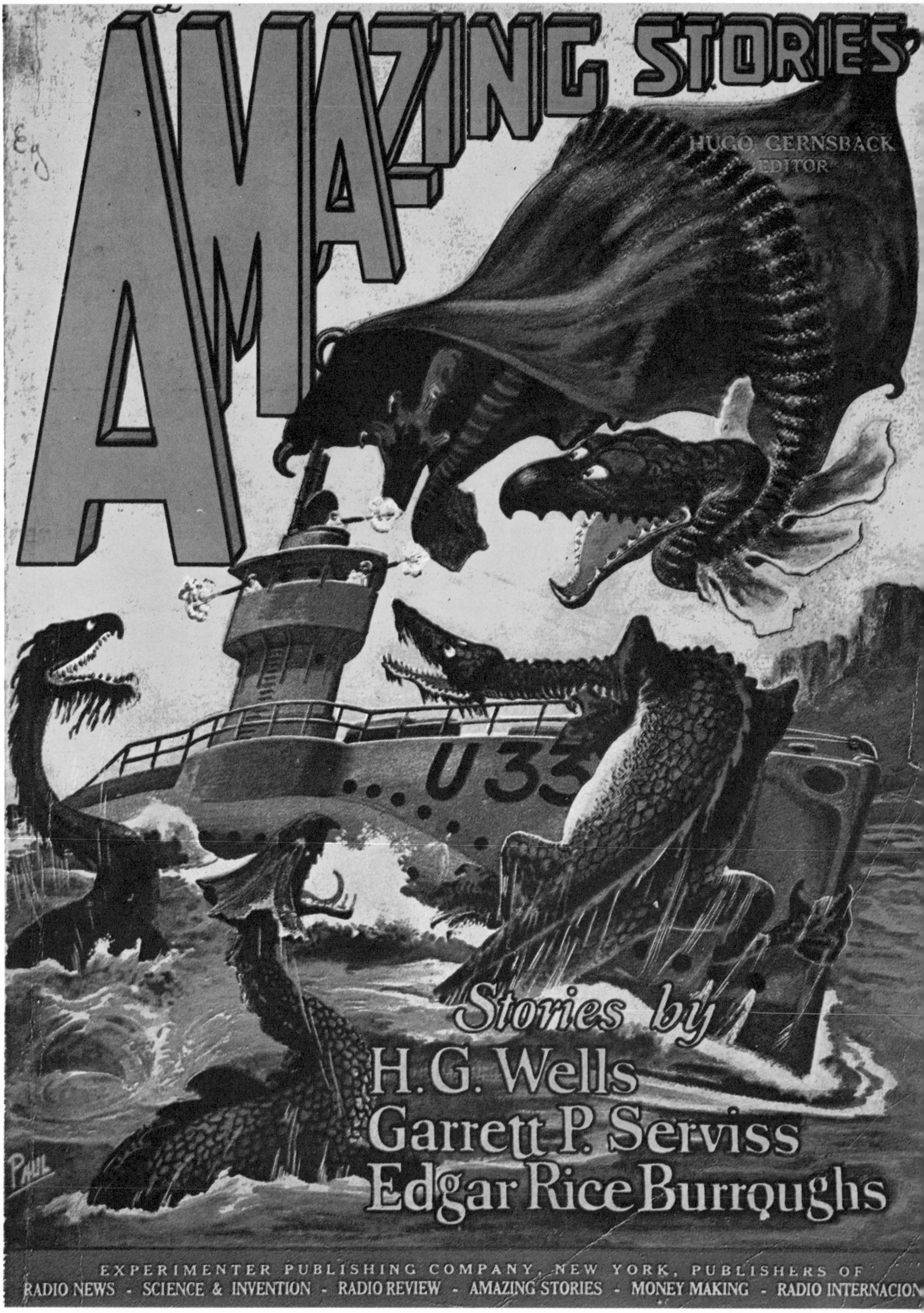

AMAZING STORIES

HUGO GERNSBACK
EDITOR

U 33

Stories by
H. G. Wells
Garrett P. Serviss
Edgar Rice Burroughs

EXPERIMENTER PUBLISHING COMPANY, NEW YORK, PUBLISHERS OF
RADIO NEWS · SCIENCE & INVENTION · RADIO REVIEW · AMAZING STORIES · MONEY MAKING · RADIO INTERNACION

(LEFT) Frank R. Paul's cover for the February 1927 issue illustrating the month's lead story, Edgar Rice Burroughs' 'The Land that Time Forgot'. This is a scene 'in which a number of pre-historic monster sea and air reptiles very nearly devour the subterranean river travelers. Fortunately for them they are able to retreat into their submarines'.

What more could one ask for in a cover? Battling it out with such creatures, even if they do look a lot less frightening than the artist would have liked, must be fun! SF art at this time was still searching for an identity, as indeed were the stories. But we see here the first flickerings of the rapidly developing form. Notice particularly the submarine, a sleek credible form not unlike a craft from the Second World War.

The colours are garish. No subtle renderings and pastel shades for Gernsback! He wanted as eye-catching a cover as possible, something that would leap out from everything else on the news-stands.

(ABOVE) 'Our cover this month depicts a scene in 'The War of the Worlds', in which three Martians, highly developed intelligencies in bodies vastly different from ours, are seen stalking in their machines, over a town near London, wreaking destruction of life and land by the use of their deadly Heat-Rays and long wiry tentacles'. Thus the inimitable 'School of Gernsback' prose on the contents page of August 1927.

Though not credited, this is the work of Frank R. Paul. It is a *tour-de-force* which pays tribute to a number of earlier Wells illustrators. The Martians do look a little more fragile than they appear in the story, their legs seem to incorporate an elementary form of clamp, and any moment might topple over. The ruins appear more like Mexican pueblos than bombed-out surburban villas, yet overall the picture is a success on its own terms. The strange colour adds to the effect.

Paul was probably reponsible for the staggering of the magazine's title. Shaded-down as the word 'Amazing' is, it certainly added to the dynamism of the supporting art work. Comparing this with other magazines where the title was boxed in, it is obvious that this arrangement allows a greater freedom.

The story by Julian Huxley was 'The Tissue Culture King', from which an illustration is reproduced on the following page.

Vol. 1
No. 2

SPRING
1928

AMAZING STORIES QUARTERLY

HUGO GERNSBACK, *Editor*

MIRIAM BOURNE, *Asso. Editor*   WILBUR C. WHITEHEAD, *Literary Editor*
Dr. T. O'CONOR SLOANE, Ph.D., *Asso. Editor*   C. A. BRANDT, *Literary Editor*
Editorial and General Offices: 230 Fifth Avenue, New York, N. Y.

The Rise of Scientifiction

By Hugo Gernsback

SINCE AMAZING STORIES and its sister magazines, AMAZING STORIES ANNUAL and AMAZING STORIES QUARTERLY came into being, a great change has taken place in scientifiction literature. When the magazine was first launched, we had no original manuscripts at all. Little by little, as the magazine continued to grow, original scientifiction manuscripts began to arrive, and it became possible to have less and less reprints. The initial issue of AMAZING STORIES contained 100% reprints, that is, stories all of which had been published before. The tendency now however, is distinctly the other way. In the current issues of AMAZING STORIES, the only reprints published are some of the stories of the Jules Verne and H. G. Wells type, for which there seems to be a constant demand by the many readers who have not seen these classics before.

When we brought out the YEAR BOOK last Summer, we featured only one original story, "The Master Mind of Mars," by Edgar Rice Burroughs. All other stories were reprints. The first QUARTERLY, three months ago, contained only one reprint—H. G. Wells' famous story, "When the Sleeper Wakes." All other stories were original.

And now, the second issue of the QUARTERLY contain 100% new stories, all of them original. This again is an experiment, in the first place, because until very recently, there were not enough new scientifiction stories to go around,

and secondly, because the few that were submitted, were not always good enough to publish.

But times are rapidly changing. Scientifiction may now be said to have arrived with a bang. More and more authors of the better kind are taking to scientifiction as the proverbial duck takes to water. It is a great source of satisfaction to us, and we point to it with pride, that 90% of the really good scientifiction authors are Americans, the rest being scattered over the world. We believe that America will in time, become known as the hotbed of scientifiction, and that more excellent scientifiction will be turned out in this country than anywhere else. Already, in our editorial opinion, our modern authors have far eclipsed both Jules Verne and H. G. Wells. We know that is a broad statement, and one of vast import, but it is true, nevertheless. It takes time for a new art to develop and while we are not as yet at the top, we are slowly getting there, certainly, and the movement of scientifiction will sooner or later assume proportions far exceeding the expectations of most of us.

Just as there are cycles in style, there are cycles in literature. During the last few decades, for instance, there were cycles of the exposé story; then we had the boys detective cycle; next the real detective stories; more recently the sex story; and still more recently, the self confession story. These are only the outstanding distinct types. Of course, there are many others. But the scientifiction cycle is now in its ascendancy and is growing rapidly.

The Next Issue of the Quarterly Will Be on the Newsstands July 20th

(ABOVE) Frank R. Paul again, for Homer Eon Flint's 'The Nth Man', Spring 1928. The story of a benign giant's tramp across America to preach crack-barrel philosophy and wisdom to the Heads of State, was tailor-made for the art department of the magazine. One sometime feels looking at these drawings that they were executed first and the story came later…

(LEFT) Hugo Gernsback's Spring 1928 editorial, a model of his bombast. The prose would do any Hollywood press agent, 1932 vintage, proud. He makes a number of perceptive predictions and some rather extravagant claims. '…our modern authors have far eclipsed both Jules Verne and H. G. Wells', no less! Gernsback was in at the birth of something which was to prove bigger than even he expected.

(BELOW) The title illustration for Julian Huxley's 'The Tissue Culture King', August 1927, is pure Grandville with one important difference, the head scratching scientist. This figure will now inform us of the steps taken in achieving these monstrous creations, 'I thought I would see whether art could not improve upon nature, and set myself to recall experimental embryology…'
Julian, the grandson of T. H. Huxley, had originally published this story in the *Yale Review* a year earlier. Gernsback was never happier than when including work by such distinguished names, seeking to gain a wider acceptance and understanding thereby. It was to be many years before SF would win the recognition it deserved.

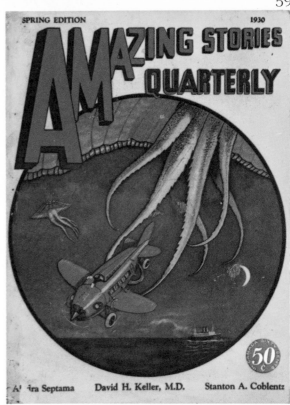

(LEFT) The cover for January 1929, by Frank R. Paul, depicts a scene from 'The Sixth Glacier' by 'Marius', in which 'the Woolworth and Munincipal Buildings, giant prides of New York, are seen giving way to the fierce strength of the on-rushing masses of ice'. A compelling and finely detailed action shot, this must be considered as one of Paul's early triumphs.

(ABOVE LEFT) Hans Wessolowski's Fall 1929 illustration for Edmond Hamilton's 'The Other Side of the Moon', in Amazing's sister publication, Amazing Stories Quarterly. The turtlemen are ill-executed and of little consequence, the girders and circular forms make some ammends.

(ABOVE RIGHT) Flying star fish, actually 'malignant intelligences of space', capturing one of our planes as featured in Aladra Septama's 'Dragons of Space'. Playful art work by Leo Morey.

(RIGHT) Paul's splendid design for a key scene in Benjamin Witwer's 'Radio Mates', July 1927. The scientist 'is ready to turn the aerial switch, which will cause his sweetheart, in the mammoth transmitter tube, to disappear gradually and be transmitted through space by ether wave action, and be reproduced at some distant point, where he expects to follow immediately in like manner!', yet!

The instrumentation here is merely the radio writ large, and the casings are bakelite.

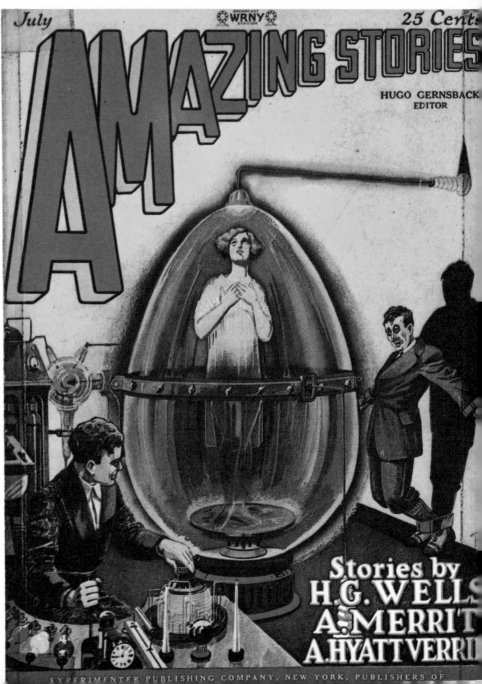

(ABOVE LEFT) Another Frank R. Paul sketch for Witwer's 'Radio Mates', July 1927. First experiments in ether wave transmission, here with a 'piglet', though it does look a little more like a hamster. The surrounding radio-set technology is credible, the scientist, with his expression of awe and excitement, even more so.

(ABOVE) Another early triumph of Paul's, December 1928. The story is Jack Williamson's 'The Metal Man'. Here we see the spaceman, (could it be Biggles' father?) being lifted by a 'scarlet fire reaching out caressingly over his body'. The six-sided crystal with its eyes of Horus is a fine conception if a little toy-like. The landscape is finely rendered.

(LEFT) Paul's lead illustration for Irvin Lester and Fletcher Pratt's 'The Roger Bacon Formula, January 1929. Like many of the artist's extraterrestials, these Venusuvians are friendly looking creatures that might be found in any child's collection of dolls. The decor here seems like *Vogu's* last word on the height of contemporary modernity. Paul frequently favoured this almost pointillistic approach to his work, an approach that was not always succesapproach that was not always successful.

(LEFT) Another Morey drawing for the mellifluously named Aladra Septama's 'Dragons of Space', *Amazing Stories Quarterly*, Spring 1930. The spaceship *Therma*, here leaving Venus with 'elementals' circling over her, looks like a cross between a dirigible and an aeroplane. It appears to be driven, in addition to the rear rocket, by four props, though to be charitable we could ascribe these to stabilisation functions. An imposing illustration which has not dated in the slightest apart from these minor details.

(RIGHT) And the cow was whisked over the moon! Leo Morey's flying star-fish for 'Dragons of Space' abducts livestock from a small New England farm. Forty years later we are told by the flying-saucer buffs that such occurences are regular wherever the saucers visit (and that all such reports are hushed up by the Men in Black from a secret Government department). Life imitating art again!

(LEFT) Morey expertly handled these larger than life creatures. This one is from David H. Keller's 'The Flying Threat', a story which explored the eugenics of insect breeding. 'If entomologists should begin to devote themselves to the further development of harmful insects or otherwise, in the form of specialised and enlarged breeding, some mighty exciting things might happen'. And mighty exciting it might be at that! *Amazing Stories Quarterly*, Spring 1930.

The Cerebral Library
by David H. Keller, M.D.

Beings of the Boundless Blue
by Walter Kateley

Through the Vibrations

Across the Void, Part II

(LEFT) Threatened by his own creation! Frank R. Paul shows us the confrontation between insect and insect-maker which is the climax to Russell Hays' story, 'The Beetle Experiment', in June 1929. The colouring and detail here blend beautifully, adding to the verisimilitude of the cover. Drawing humans was not one of Paul's stronger points, they often look too much like mannequins, rigid and without just proportions.

(ABOVE LEFT) May 1931 was an early colour cover triumph for Morey. The imp like creatures arise from a volcano amid the rich hues of orange and red 'preparatory to making another raid in the vicinity of Kilauea'. If the beings lack much detail these are more than compensated for by their do-it-yourself back-packs and belts (send $3.50 to …). The story is Wood Peters' 'The Great Catastrophe of 2947.'

(ABOVE RIGHT) The multi-legged metal man ambles across a most convincing townscape as envisaged by Morey for John B. Harris' 'The Lost Machine', April 1932. SF's reply to Marcel Duchamp's 'Nude Descending a Staircase'?

(BELOW LEFT) Morey again. A fine realisation for Neil R. Jones' 'The Return of the Tripeds', May 1932.

(BELOW RIGHT) An earlier Morey cover, from November 1930. The Fiend-without-a-body arises from the waves to clutch the heroes of R. F. Starzl's 'The Globoid Terror'. A real eye-catching cover, exactly as Hugo Gernsback instructed.

Scientific Fiction by:

David H. Keller, M.D.
Neil R. Jones
Stephen G. Hale
Miles J. Breuer, M.D.

NOVEMBER

THE DRUMS OF TAPAJOS
By Capt. S. P. MEEK, U.S.A.

Other scientifiction stories by:

R. F. STARZL
JOHN W. CAMPBELL, Jr.
JACK WILLIAMSON

(LEFT) Hans Wessolowski's June 1932 cover for John W. Campbell's 'When the Atoms Failed'. Here we see the Martian visitors 'arriving in their interplanetary cruisers, fitted out for attack with atomic weapons hanging from the bottoms of their ships'. Campbell, who is described in the story's blurb as 'our new author…a student at the Massachusetts Institute of Technology, (who) shows (a) marvellous ability at combining science with romance', was later to become the editor of *Astounding* and it was he, rather than Gernsback, who moulded the disparate elements of the genre into what we now know as SF.

(ABOVE LEFT) Psychedelia, art-deco style. Imaginative swirls drawn by Wessolowski for A Hyatt Verrill's 'Vampires of the Desert', in which prehistoric fossil seeds are brought to life in South America. December 1929.

(ABOVE RIGHT) A transparent space ship reveals its inner-most secret electrical generators and radio-set furbishings as the two heroes are whisked off to another planet in 'A Baby on Neptune', by Clare Winger Harris and Miles J. Breuer. Gernsback, himself a pioneer in radio, left a rich legacy in this type of imagery, valves, condensers, and such. Illustration by Wessolowski. December 1929.

(RIGHT) Moonmen! Should you not recognise the figure on the right, it is Aparo 'the Lunarian leader…who was later to appear on the world's television screens'. Notice again the ubiquitous electrical-generator inspired device to the rear. A jokey representation from John Edwards' 'Masters of the Earth' by Morey, June 1932. Why are extra-terrestials so often unconvincing?

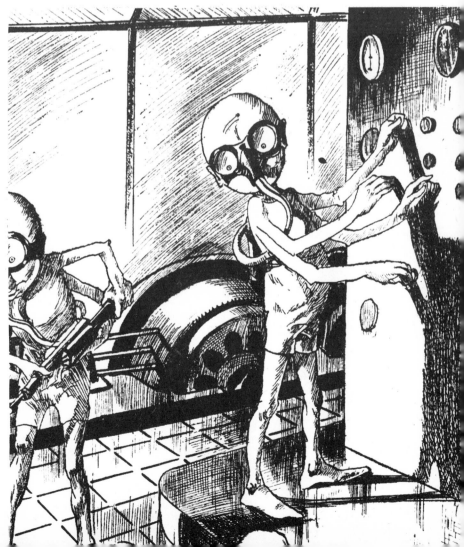

(LEFT) Undoubtedly an inter-galactic *ampallang!* Morey must have got his inspiration for this space-ship from the pages of a Japanese rubber-goods catalogue, rendered as it is in the original in latex-like orange. The figure in the foreground appears stern and omnipotent, obviously someone to be reckoned with in the story of 'The Terror Out of Space' by a writer who shares his name with that of an approach to Hampstead, Haverstock Hill. February 1934.

(BELOW LEFT) A slightly more imaginative and rather Gothic inspired cover by Morey in July 1935. Reminiscent of a surrealist collage, it seems to work far more on its own terms than many of the artist's strict technological designs. The story is A. Hyatt Verrill's 'The Inner World', a saga of hollow earth adventures where Dr Thurlow 'supposed to be long dead' meets the Tss'Zors 'a mixture of octopus, ant, human being, and bat'. July 1935.

(ABOVE) Off to the stars and no messing! The cover art-work now begins to assume the identity we associate with the genre. The out and out space-opera of inter-galactic travel and mind-boggling adventures. Sleek ships soaring through the ether into the unknown. Executed by Morey in October 1935 for George H. Scheer's 'Another Dimension'. This was the year that the Americans, Stevens and Anderson, beat existing records in ascending to a height of 74,000 feet in a helium balloon. It is not recorded whether the fledgling astronauts took any copies of *Amazing* with them. It would be touching to think they did!

(RIGHT) One of Morey's finest covers to date. A superb creation, if a little reminiscent of somebody else's work, that does full justice to Neil R. Jones' story 'The Music Monsters' in April 1938.

AMAZING STORIES

April, 1938
25 Cents

THE MUSIC MONSTERS

by

NEIL R. JONES

J. LEWIS BURTT
JOHN RUSSELL FEARN

(LEFT AND RIGHT) June 1938 and August 1938 respectively. The former is credited to Horace Hime and Frank Lewis, the latter to Henry F. Kroeger. The current editors of *Amazing*, obviously feeling that it was time they started taking advantage of the wonders of technology they were continually extolling in the pages of the magazine, had a brief flirtation with photographic covers. The results speak for themselves. The June cover is meritous of an Anya Seton story, had she ever decided to write for the pulps, while the August offering, nastily sadistic, looks more like the sado-masochism of the 'Jim Bondage' strip cartoon. The first cover did not relate to any story in particular while the second was for Robert Bloch's 'Secret of the Observatory' in which 'The kinetic energy camera delves weirdly into a startling secret'! Some camera!

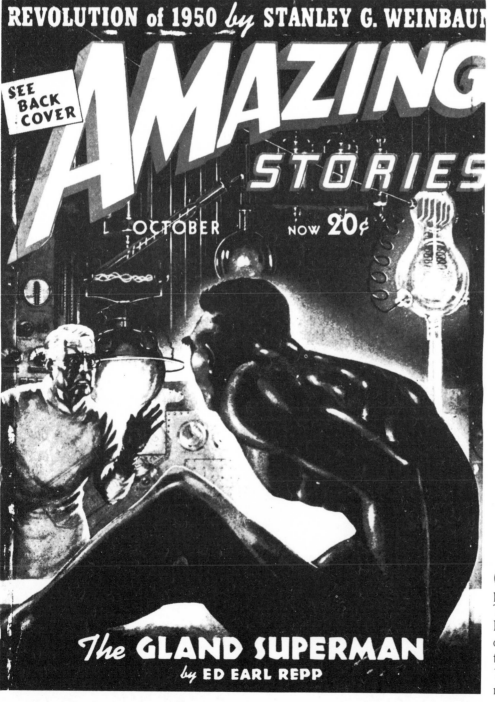

(LEFT) The props and gadge have finally broken away from th fixation with the insides of rad sets to rake on new and mc credible forms as shown in t superbly detailed cover by Rob Fuqua. In terms of technique t painting is a considerable advar on the more rudimentary style's Paul, Morey and Wessolowski. T execution of the highlights on t back of the foreground figure more formal and professiona conceived than much that h passed. The lucky author was Earl Repp, and his story, 'The Gla Superman'. October 1938.

(RIGHT) Another Robert Fuqu painting, this time for Richai Tooker's 'Ray of Eternity' i November 1938. A rather horrei dous cover more befitting perhaj the front of that rival pulp, *Wei Tales*. Fine detailing again vei much in evidence.

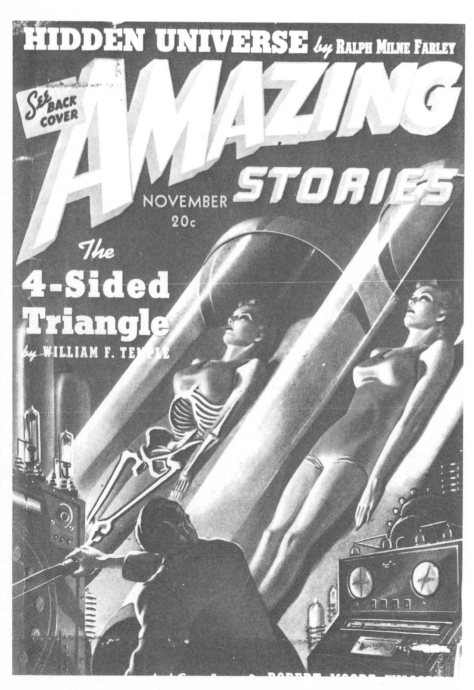

(ABOVE LEFT) 'These cubical beings have established themselves as favourites with our readers and in this story a decidedly new touch is given to their adventures'. Thus reads the introductory blurb to Neil R. Jones' 'Twin Worlds', April 1937. Leo Morey was given another opportunity to depict the quadruped boxes which are seen here taking the road to Mandalay (or, if you are more at home in another tradition, Xanadu). The sweeping road leads across the bridge and to a castle which looks distinctly like a period cigarette lighter. A rather dull landscape.

(ABOVE CENTRE) Robert Fuqua's August 1939 depiction of the David and Goliath confrontation in 'Warrior of Mars' by Arthur R. Tofte. This seems to lack the usual polish of the artist's work. The foreground figure appears to have a withered right arm. The giant looks inflatable.

(ABOVE RIGHT) The 'three Americans and a Maya girl (who) venture into the jungles of Yucatan to do battle with Satan himself', as featured in Robert Moore Williams' 'Return of Satan', October 1939, seem to have given Fuqua a little more inspiration for this action-packed cover. The encased brain and the device which is emitting rays of lightening serve almost as SF archetypes.

(LEFT) The pioneer British SF writer William Temple was well served with H. W. McCauley's cover for 'The 4-sided Triangle', his most famous story. The gadgetry again looks suspiciously like the inside of a radio, probably because the writer was a newcomer to the field. The two women, encased in plastic, are very much alive. November 1939.

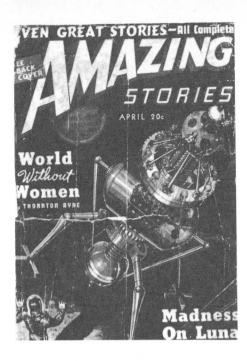

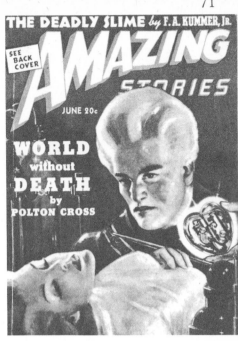

(ABOVE LEFT) The genre continues to take shape! Or why every schoolmaster of the day violently condemned SF as worthless. Resembling some grotesque of Posada's, this cover by Fuqua hardly gives a hint of the considered writing within. Still, it sold the magazine The highly decorated crustacean is worthy of a few square centimetres on any Bosch canvas, while the giant would take prime place in an SF bestiary. The story was by Festus Pragnell, 'Ghost of Mars', December 1938.

(ABOVE CENTRE) Exciting technological high-jinks with this space vehicle! a remarkably modern looking device with lots to gloat over. One can hear it whizzing and whirring as it makes its way towards the helmeted figure in the foreground. A scene from Thornton Ayres' 'World Without Women', April 1939, in which Perry Mills patterns 'a synthetic body in Kay Wancliffe's image. But he could not make it live. Extinction faced mankind. Then, incredibly, the lifeless body spoke…' Now, in the words of Philip Wylie, 'Take your three dots, damn you!'

(ABOVE RIGHT) The figure with the bouffant hair-do holds a replacement heart, replete with cogs, levers, and ratchets. None of that effeminate transistor soft-ware here! Cover painting by William Juhre for Polton Cross' story, 'World Without Death'. 'No one was dying and disaster threatened the world because of overcrowding. What could be done?' June 1939.

(RIGHT) Two superbly conceived ships soar through the Solar System past Mars in Julien S. Krupa's cover for Henry Gade's 'Liners of Space', December 1939.

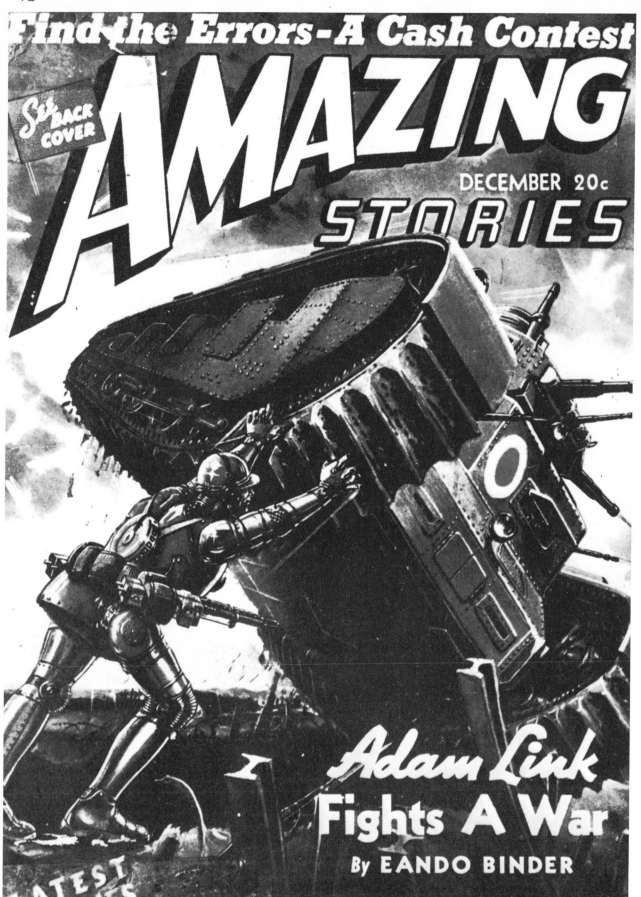

Find the Errors - A Cash Contest

See BACK COVER

AMAZING

DECEMBER 20c

STORIES

Adam Link

Fights A War

BY EANDO BINDER

(ABOVE) As soon as the Second World War began it proved to be grist in the mills of the SF writers. A whole new stock of characters and situations presented themselves for inclusion in these technological reveries. Belligerent Martians, evil Venusuvians, wicked Lunarmen, none of them seemed quite so exciting now that there were real foes across the Atlantic and Pacific Oceans. The inclusion of Germans, or Japanese, or Italians, made the stories much more immediate, added to their impact. Topicality became the order of the day as in this illustration, by Fuqua, for Eando (i.e. E. and O.) Binder's 'Adam Link fights a War'. 'Adam Link constructed his robots for peace, to prove their worth in Man's world. But when the crushing Panzer blitzkrieg surged over the Mexican border, he had to lead them to war'.

The blood-and-guts-and-glory approach to militarism… The story dates from December 1940. Pearl Harbour was now only several issues of *Amazing* away…

CHAPTER FIVE

'There must be a scientific explanation!' ~ASTOUNDING.

American pulp publishing in the 1920s and 1930s was a jungle of incest with the rival chains feeding on each other's success and failure. The newsagents' stands were aglow with the screaming logos and punchy artwork of periodicals like *Fight Stories*, *Over the Top* (Frontline Fighting Stories), *Racketeer Stories*, *Pep Stories*, *Ranch Romances*, *Weird Tales* (one of the few to transcend its age. It published much SF.), *The Thrill Book*, *The Wizard* (fictional 'adventures in money making', no less!), not to mention the whole series of *Spicy* this and *Spicy* that. Gernsback had published the first *Amazing* in April 1926. Two years later it was still flourishing. And, a further two years on, while still continuing, it occured to W. L. Clayton, another magazine entrepreneur, that the market could support yet another SF pulp. Thus January 1930 saw the arrival of a new offering, running to some 144 pages (248mm by 172mm) of the same indescribable stock, with the glorious name of *Astounding Stories of Super-Science*.

In *Astounding's* early years science was merely something that gave an added fillip or two to the action packed adventures which, very nearly, could almost have appeared in any other non-SF pulp. There was no pretence, *à la* Gernsback, to present science either credibly or educationally (not that Gernsback's approach *ever* really succeeded).

In February 1931 the magazine's name was changed to *Astounding Stories*, and it was later changed yet again, in March 1938, to *Astounding Science Fiction* (it still appears regularly today, but under the name of *Analog*, a change dating from October 1960).

Astounding, in the early 1930s, did every bit as much as *Amazing* in creating the impression of SF being little more than BEMs and space-opera extravaganzas. All this would radically change after 1937 when a young and able SF writer, John W. Campbell was appointed as the new editor. Campbell was to be the greatest editor in the history of the genre to date, and SF, as we know it now, is largely the result of his ideas. He impressed on the writing a discipline and logic which it desperately sought and awoke his contributors to a responsibility which they scarcely thought existed. While Campbell had many faults both as an editor and thinker, his espousal of the dubious ideas promulgated by L. Ron Hubbard springs particularly to mind, the form of present day mainstream SF is his epitaph.

The cover and interior artwork of *Astounding*, notably in its earlier years, vied with the garish and wild productions of Gernsback. Hans Waldemar Wessolowski, who signed, simply Wesso, a graduate of *Amazing*, contributed many fine covers and, later, black and white illustrations. *Astounding's* great discoveries in the 1930s though were undoubedly Howard V. Brown (actually he had in fact worked very briefly for Gernsback twenty years earlier), for the covers, and Eliott Dold for the insides. A remarkable combination of talents as will be seen . . .

Hans Wessolowski's playful and art nouveau inspired cover for *Astounding*, April 1932, suggested by a scene in Charles Willard Diffin's 'The Finding of Haldgren'; 'Chet Bullard Answers the Pinpoint of Light That from the Craggy Desolation of the Moon Stabs Out Man's Old Call for Help', sic, is the introduction.

(ABOVE AND LEFT) Social creepy-crawlies have the disturbing habit of becoming remarkably unsocial when invested with intelligence. A compelling theme here exercised in one of the also-rans, Paul Ernst's 'The Raid on the Termites', June 1932. Wesso's two illustrations more than flatter the story. The sketch above captures the torso armour of the termites very convincingly, while the cover termite, even if it does look like an escapee from the bendy-toy factory, still radiates a powerful sense of menace.

(RIGHT) Some nicely conceived hardware is the backdrop for this scene from Hal K. Wells' 'The Cavern of the Shining Ones', November 1932. Wesso's double-yolked spectre would have been a credit to a séance stage managed by Eusapia Palladino. The three resolute figures are not, as has been suggested, George Orwell, T.E. Lawrence, and Arthur Koestler (reading left to right), but 'Husky Down and Outers' (!?) hired by 'Layroh…for his expedition (which) is part of a plan made ages past'. Now you know.

20¢

ASTOUNDING STORIES

THE RAID ON THE TERMITES
By PAUL ERNST
And
TWO THOUSAND MILES BELOW
An Amazing New Mid-Earth Novel

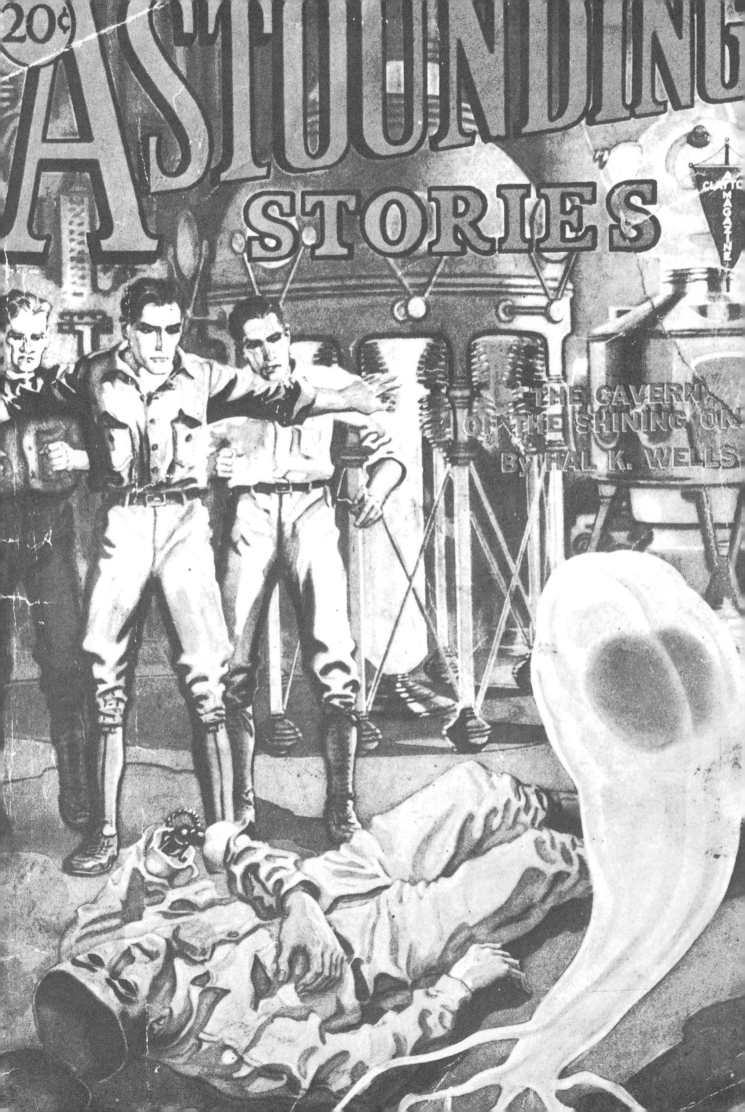

(ABOVE LEFT) One of Wesso's more thought provoking covers. It was originally executed for E. E. Smith's classic 'Triplanetary' series which should have begun in this March 1933 issue. As it was the story finally appeared in the rival *Amazing* one year later. Rather than waste good art work, it was used none the less, here supposedly representing Jack Williamson's 'Salvage in Space'.

(ABOVE RIGHT UPPER) Mark Marchioni's interior sketch for the aforementioned Williamson story. The ethereal monster with its outstretched claw contrasts well with the solid astronaut figures.

(ABOVE RIGHT LOWER) Gruesome cross-eyed spiders from Sewell Peaslee Wright's 'The Death Traps of FX-31' threaten Wessoo's animated humans as they make a bid for freedom. March 1933.

(LEFT) *Astounding* changed ownership and this October 1933 cover was the first to be published under the new imprint of Street and Smith. Gone was Hans Wessolowski, in his place, Howard V. Brown, whose debut was anthing but SF, as indeed were most of the contents. For a time it appeared as if *Astounding* had foresaken the genre and plumped for general occult and high adventure stories instead.

(RIGHT) Howard V. Brown's on-rushing ship, resembling some vast galactic torpedo, signalled the first installment of E. E. Smith's 'The Skylark of Valeron' in August 1934. The detail of the craft is perfect, right down to the rivets strung along the joins of steel sheeting. And should any moon shots have been attempted in the 1930s, this is exactly how the ships would have appeared.

A STREET & SMITH PUBLICATION

ASTOUNDING

STOR

AUGU

BRITISH
EDITION
—
Atlas Publishing &
Distributing Co., Ltd.,
LONDON :: E.C.4

1S

The
SKY
LARK
of
Valeron
by
EDWARD
E.
SMITH, Ph.D.

(ABOVE) Elliot Dold's interior illustration for E. E. Smith's 'The Skylark of Valeron', August 1934. 'The dummy that was DuQuesne whirled, snarling, and its automatic pistol and that of its fellow dummy were leaping out when a magnetic force snatched away their weapons and a heat ray of prodigous power reduced the effigies to two piles of grey ashes. And DuQuesne, motionless inside his space suit, waited ....

The saturnine figure, aghast at its gun having been wrenched from its grip, is a credit to Dold, conveying as it does the drama and speed of the scene. The background gadgetry is a pleasant mess of plumber's and radio repair-man's spare parts, while the hand gun must have been waiting impatiently for the arrival of Flash Gordon.

(RIGHT) Jack Williamson's 'The Legion of Space', August 1934, was graced with this fine example of Elliot Dold's work. The monstrous rubbery creature with its playing tentacles encircling the hapless humans deserves a place in any cosmic bestiary. Dold's drawings, while often lacking the wild technological imagination of a Frank R. Paul, were often infused with a drama and urgency that escaped the other illustrators.

(BELOW) The heading design for the serialisation of Charles Fort's great collection of mysterious and unexplained phenomena, *Lo!*, August 1934. Though uncredited, it is probably by Dold. It is a masterly rendering, and one of the few examples of 1930s pulp art whose baroque is comparable with the classical tradition of grotesques. The intertwined and tumbling frogs go beyond being a mere illustration to Fort's documentation of 'strange' rainfalls and other curiosa and take on the power of an apocalyptic vision. (But is it SF…?).

A STREET & SMITH PUBLICATION

ASTOUNDING STORIES

JUNE 20¢

CONTENTS COPYRIGHTED 1935

THE INVADERS

by

DON A. STUART

NRA CODE

ALAS,
ALL THINKING
by
HARRY BATES

(ABOVE UPPER RIGHT) A haunting depiction of a strange alien intelligence sensitively rendered by Dold for Harry Bates' 'Alas, All Thinking!' The caption reads, 'Why should he move?' A lingering question…Notice the fine formal detailing here. June 1935.

(ABOVE LEFT) Howard V. Brown's covers were going from strength to strength, and were incredibly imaginative canvases assaulting the readers' eye. The dispassionate intelligence is resolute in the face of the frail human with outstretched arms clambering to save a young woman from some unimaginable fate. The photographic-like quality of Brown's technique further convinces us of the authenticity of the scene. The lead story was Don A. Stuart's (a pseudonym of Campbell's) 'The Invaders'. 'Three thousand years have elapsed since the Machine stopped working…'

(ABOVE, LOWER RIGHT AND LEFT) Elliot Dold's interiors for the same story have a more violent and neurotic quality than Brown's cover. The creatures have withered somewhat in their flight across the pages and here appear less credible. 'Jan felt two powerful hands grip his arms, and two powerful feet take hold of his legs! Meg was caught too, and was fighting as hard as he'. A particularly fine touch here is the vignetting of the conflict by the overhanging foliage.

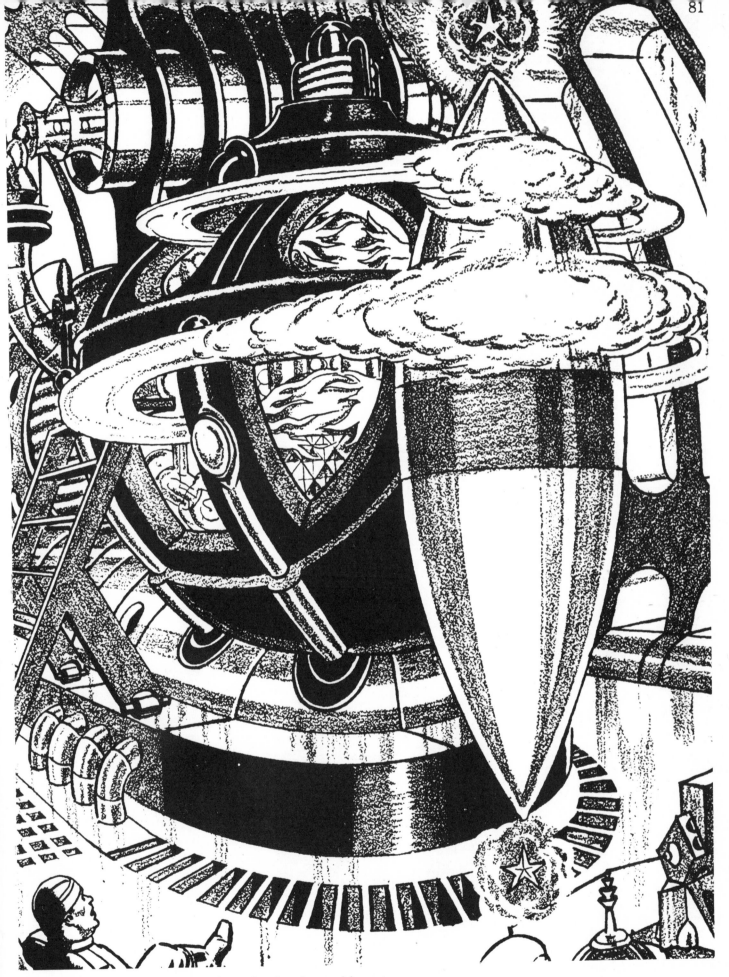

Mark Marchioni's grab-bag of technology adds up to an over-powering image of a machine-dominated future, a total hardware world, with man a mere appendage. 'It came across the floor, to the precious generator. The green-white mist swirled out, reached into them...' Now read on! The story was Jack Williamson's 'The Cometeers' (part two) in June 1936, a space-opera extravaganza.

(LEFT) Almost like props from a child's conjuring set, these composite creatures, part lobster, part vacuum cleaner, and part citrus fruit, have a jokey and playful countenance as with many other of Brown's creations. The colour is subdued and skillfully handled. Cover for 'The Shadow Out of Space' by H. P. Lovecraft, June 1936.

(BELOW LEFT) The strange colour of Howard V. Brown again, three months later in September 1936. As the rest of the world was flocking to read a book which begun with the statement that 'Scarlett O'Hara was not beautiful', SF readers were burying themselves in Donald Wandrei's highly original 'Finality Unlimited', from whence the cover. Brown's painting, with its hint of the Byzantine, depicts some very stimulating forms and gadgets — notably the instrument encased in the glass dome.

(BELOW CENTRE) Brown's October 1936 cover seemed to lack the sparkle and deftness of much of his earlier work. The detail is fudged and the colour poor. The only dynamism here is that of the bold and proclaiming typography of the magazine's title. The lucky author was Raymond Z. Gallun with 'Godson of Almarlu'.

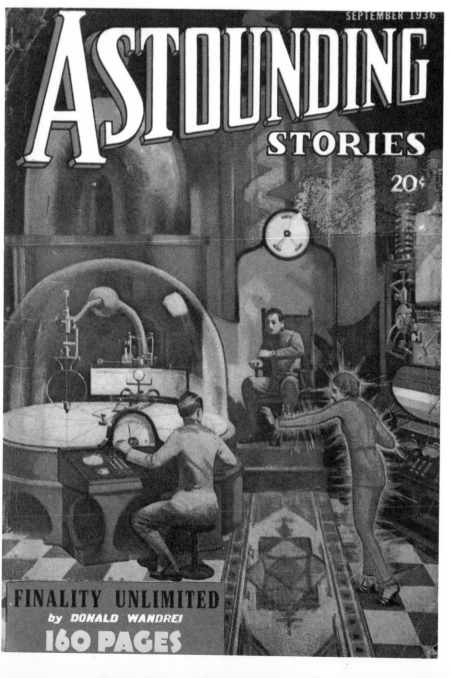

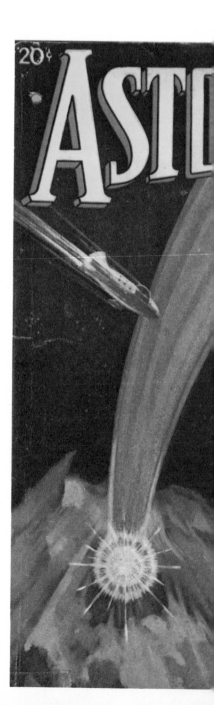

(RIGHT) Looking more like a sun-lamp session in a Bavarian naturist clinic, circa 1933, Brown's painting for Warner van Lorne's 'Other Space' in May 1937, has the photographic-like quality we associate with his work. Perhaps the subject matter of the earlier October 1936 cover was not something that brought out the best in him. Here, with a fine opportunity for detail, the art work leaps from the page and intrigues.

(BELOW RIGHT) Brown's adroit handling of the white planet's surface and the surrounding aura of orange very nearly rescue the overall conception. The insignificant space vehicle, drifting without purpose apparently, looks as though it might fall off the bottom of the page any moment. Viewed upside down the painting becomes more three dimensional and dynamic — an interesting example of Slavko Vorkapich's Behaviourist musings on 'up' and 'down' movement. The cover story was 'Water for Mars' by Ross Rocklynne, April 1937.

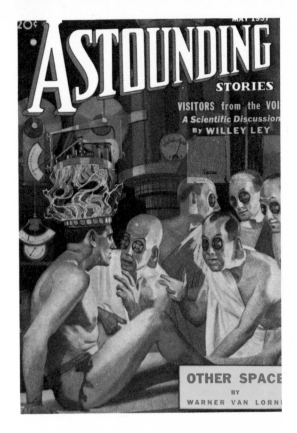

(ABOVE) A splendid psychadelic crustacean soars through the universe: 'Truly I had become a rider of Pegasus! My steed came from who knows what shadowy corner of the universe!' Thus Lothar Weiss, the hero of Raymond Z. Gallun's 'A Beast of the Void', September 1936. The blurb on the contents page invitingly inquires, 'Might not nature contrive a creature to fly through interplanetary space?' The illustration is uncredited. Possibly by Wesso.

(BELOW) The running head for *Astounding*'s regular letters-to-the-editor feature, ironically titled with reference to the hardware of an earlier age, 'Lets Get Down to Brass Tacks'. The readers were outspoken — urging the editor to fire Wesso because 'he can't draw to save his life', or to reinstate Paul, or to give yet another illustrator 'a holiday for keeps'. A comprehensive collection of these letters spanning the first thirty years of SF magazines would give an unique insight to the reader-writer relationship and the growth of the genre.

(ABOVE) A richly imaginative and impressive drawing by Wesso took the honours in this June 1937 issue. The geometry of the interplaying lights centred on the hydro-encephalic figure give the execution an added form. 'Erasmus was about to blurt something when the creature stopped him with a wave of

thought. 'You need not say it, merely think', it explained. 'You are wondering what I am. At one time I was known as Edward Berkeley, a human scientist — your old friend, Era!'
'What has happened to you?' gasped the dazed little physicist. 'And what has happened to all the other people around here?'

Something equivalent to a mental chuckle issued from the monster. 'Not merely the people around here, but the entire world is affected by the Change!'
The story is an intriguing exploration of anti-Darwinism by Oliver Saari, 'Two Sane Men'.

ASTOUNDING STORIES

THE GOLDEN HORSESHOE
A Science-fiction Novel of Yellowstone
by Arthur J. Burks

In this issue: Nat Schachner, Warner Van Lorne, John W. Campbell, Jr., Eric Frank Russell, Dr. E. E. Smith

(RIGHT) The period Wesso had passed specialising only in black and white interior illustration for *Astounding* had proven a time of consolidation, for when he finally re-appeared on the cover, his work was showing a great advancement. Witness this epic painting for June 1937, where the elaborate pastel-shaded detail of the spheres and wall completely overpowers the regimentation of the spectators amassed in the shadow of the machinery. The column-supported serpentine pipeline seems to have been added as an afterthought, as a balance within the composition, it seems at odds with the surround. Here we feel Wesso may have been touching his hat to the earlier work of Frank R. Paul. The story was Nat Schachner's 'Earthspin', a memorable space-opera.

(LEFT) 'A science fiction novel of Yellowstone Park' seems an unlikely description for an original and exciting story, but Arthur J. Burks' 'The Golden Horseshoe', November 1937, was just that. 'You know…queer fancies come to a chap in a place like this. Yellowstone Park, where the earth is still young! Where it ain't yet reached the Ice Age! Where everything is so close to things as they were in the days of the great reptiles! Take Old Faithful, for instance, with its strangely erratic periods of erruption. I get that feeling of vast awesome machinery, miles below the surface, that isn't running exactly right! You know, that has something wrong with its carburettor, a blown gasket, a cracked piston ring perhaps…' And Wesso was not slow in picturing a cross-section showing the array of machines responsible for the geysers. Vast towering columns arising from the depths of the Earth, dwarfing the subterraneans.

(RIGHT) In September 1937 John W. Campbell was appointed the new editor of *Astounding*. His editorship would prove to be the most influential in the development of the genre over the next fifty years. One of his first changes was to retitle the magazine. Hitherto it had been *Astounding Stories*, now it was to be *Astounding Science Fiction* — Science Fiction and no messing! Alva Rogers notes that Campbell thought the original name 'lacked dignity, was too pulpishly sensational, and failed to accurately identify the contents between the covers' (*A Requiem for Astounding*, Chicago 1964, p.50 — the only book the present writer knows which gives a vivid impression of what it must have actually been like to read the pulps in the 1930s). His ambition was to phase out the name *Astounding* altogether so it would eventually be known as *Science Fiction*. An ambition he would have realised had not a rival *pulpeteer* issued a new magazine with just such a title. The Wesso cover to the right was the first to feature the science fiction logo and illustrates Dow Elstar's 'Something from Jupiter', a tale of one man's fight 'for his planet among the alien life-forms of another world'. The copper coloured robot is a stimulating creation which contrasts well with the figure rendered in pale electric blue.

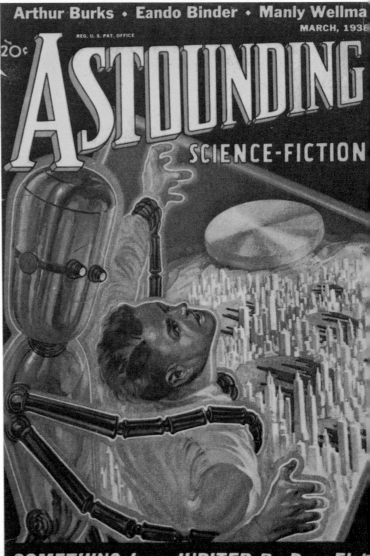

(ABOVE) Jack Binder's sensitive and thoughtful rendition of E. and O. Binder's 'Queen of the Skies', November 1937. The decoration within the ship, actually a vast city suspended some eighteen miles above the earth, populated by Viking descendants who were exiled to the skies by the Atlanteans, has an almost art nouveau quality. As do the two aesthetic young men who are waiting 'breathlessly, could this truly miraculous instrument do what they said it would?' Read on!

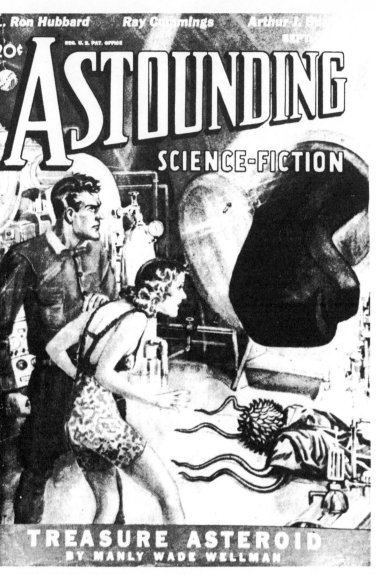

ASTOUNDING
SCIENCE-FICTION

TREASURE ASTEROID
BY MANLY WADE WELLMAN

ASTOUNDING
SCIENCE-FICTION

"HELL SHIP" by Arthur J. Burks

(ABOVE LEFT) Perhaps SF cover artists are only as good as the stories they have to illustrate? Not that they were ever renowned for reading the texts. But when a story is something like Manly Wade Wellman's 'Treasure Asteroid', we are given a comensurate cover, as with this example by an illustrator who signs, Thomson. A dreary affair and very evocative of the 1930s. The man with the clenched fist, knitted brow, and obvious concentration is THINKING, Roland Barthes having just explained to him how the higher cerebration is conveyed in the popular arts. The juxtaposition of the iron fist (without its velvet glove) and the wilted flower figure is a moving contrast. The come-on synopsis beneath the story's title on the contents page is a gem. 'She was the clinging vine type. She clung like a leech, with a predilection to trouble. Which she gathered in large quantities for ace space-pilot Drury Bannion to harvest'.

(ABOVE RIGHT) Arthur J. Burks' 'Hell Ship' in August 1938, was almost a *Boys Own Paper* yarn with a futuristic setting. 'Josh McNab, good Scots engineer, finds himself up against a cracked rotor-shaft and a bull-headed skipper aboard the space ship *Arachne*!' Wesso's painting more than sells the illusion with its criss-crossing tension of steel girders and spiral forms.

(RIGHT) A hauntingly drawn image by Jack Binder again, for a long forgotten story by Clifton B. Kruse, 'The Incredible Visitor', May 1938. With the elimination of the tiny ship at the bottom of the bubble, the man and woman suspended in the circle of light against the heavens would serve as an evocative frontispiece for a collection of Coventry Patmore's 'eternal love' poems.

Harl Vincent – L. Ron Hubbard – Nat Schachner

20¢

ASTOUNDING

NOV. 1938

SCIENCE-FICTION

JUPITER SEEN FROM GANYMEDE

REUNION ON GANYMEDE *by Clifford D. Simak*

(LEFT) This strikingly realistic view of Jupiter from its moon, Ganymede, which we could almost believe was reproduced from some 21st century *Baedker*, graced the November 1938 issue and was a fine interpretation of Clifford D. Simak's 'Reunion on Ganymede'.

Notice here the typographical arrangement and styling of the cover. Particularly the shaded-down three-dimensional serifs of the title, a bold and demonstrative assertion of the magazine's contents. The next month would see a sleeker and more streamlined design with the word 'Astounding' spread across the top of the page in uniform height sans-serifs – and a rather cold mono-tone sans-serif at that! (The legacy of Eric Gill who had 'borrowed' the typeface especially designed for the London Underground Railway in 1918 by Edward Johnson).

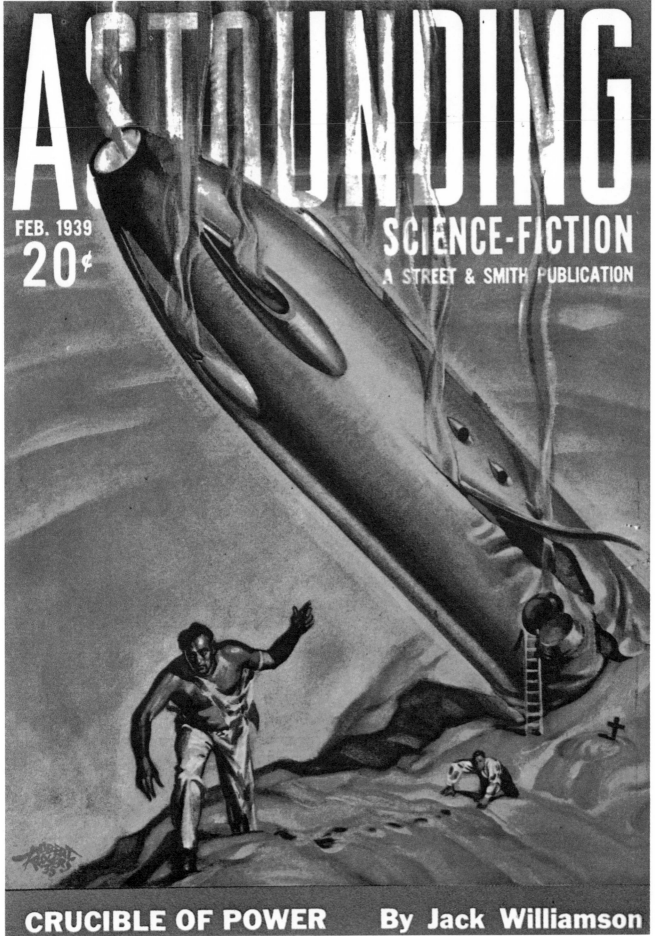

CRUCIBLE OF POWER By Jack Williamson

(RIGHT) The February 1939 issue was the third re-designed cover, and it contrasts sadly with the dramatic styling of the earlier format (today's *format* is tomorrow's *doormat*).

The February cover was by Hubert Rogers who subsequently became the resident colour man for *Astounding* throughout the 1940s (a period, considered by many, to be the Golden Age of the magazine). Considering this was the first illustration by Rogers, a scene from Jack Williamson's 'Crucible of Power', a crashed ship on the deserts of Mars, it shows his ability in matching a conception with its execution. An accomplished debut.

(ABOVE) Douglas Aiken, a 'brilliant young psychologist', calls in Dr. Ernest Coss, 'America's most brilliant physicist', in the hope that the Dr. may be able to provide an explanation for the destructive madness which is sweeping the USA. Coss, by channeling cosmic waves onto a specially constructed screen, views a man from 'Ultra-Earth…in a cube of transparent stuff, shooting queer polychrome rays of madness across America'. The scene is well rendered by Wesso with an extravaganza of technological forms towering over the protagonists as they are confronted by the cube illuminated in a cathedral-like shaft of light. The story was the concluding part of Nat Schachner's 'Simultaneous Worlds', December 1938.

CHAPTER SIX

IN A COSMIC (?) COLONY...

What had happened in Britain in the thirty years since the publication of H. G. Wells's scientific romances in the 1890s? The answer, simply, was very little, or rather, very little that would be of interest to anyone other than the dedicated chronicler of SF. As Philip Harbottle has noted in a perceptive essay — once the devotee had exhausted Wells and Verne in his local free library he had little option but to mine contemporary juvenalia should he wish to read anything remotely similar. And certainly even then the most to expect was a rip-off of *The Time Machine* or *The War of the Worlds* (Harbottle's excursion into the early years of British SF, 'A History of British Science Fiction Magazines', appears in an anthology, *Beyond this Horizon,* Sunderland, 1973, notable for its twelve pages of acutely embarassing SF *poetry.* This must have made more fans reach for their *Gernsback* than anything yet published).

The first British publication devoted exclusively to SF (though perhaps we are stretching the term here) was initially aimed at a younger audience and bore the curious name *Scoops.* It was a weekly published by C. Arthur Pearson (popular 'mags' and Boy Scout books) and first appeared in February, 1934. It ran for a little over a dozen issues and, in the later numbers, assumed more of a Gernsbackian air, a reflection of the increased availability of the American pulps on news-stands in London. Its cover art work was inconsequential, and unperturbed by Frank R. Paul's innovations.

SF by the mid-1930s had a strong and active following in Britain and several native writers were already making regularly appearances as contributors in the pages of *Amazing* and *Astounding.*

It was not until 1937 that a magazine appeared in Britain which could be compared favourably with the American productions. This was Walter Gillings' *Tales of Wonder,* published by the World's Work in Surrey, which was printed on the same harsh stock and bound within a colour cover. It ran for fifteen issues and ended in 1942, a victim of the paper shortage.

Tales of Wonder, issue no. 12. A typical British cover of the pre-war period emulating the School of Gernsback.

The incomparable *Scoops.* These two examples of its covers may be considered among the more notable.

(LEFT) Volume 1, No. 10, 14 April, 1934, shows a robot figure who is either flexing his muscles above a terror stricken city, or dancing the rumba. A stark composition bereft of detail which has an appeal transcending its origin.

(RIGHT) In sharp contrast, the first cover, February 1934, reflecting the schoolboy market at which it was aimed. One expects to find within the magazine easy to follow plans for building the mechanical man in Meccano. Artists unknown.

(LEFT) Though uncredited, this cover may well be the work of Howard V. Brown. This inter-galactic Noah's Ark is one of the most memorable ships ever to grace an SF pulp. *Startling Stories*, November 1939.

(RIGHT) Gee-whiz! again. The January 1940, *Fantastic Adventures*, by H. W. McCauley is a hard-hitting speedy conception owing something to the crime pulps. The scooter-robot is a fearful creation with a voice-grill that resembles bared teeth. If the NYPD (or any other police department for that matter) ever employs automatons to patrol the streets, one feels sure they would look like this. The cover story was Robert Williams' 'The Robot Peril', in which Blaine Rising and Marcella Kingman (English fans read 'Bob Temple' & 'Janet Hodges') become terrified when they discover 'the meaning of the word *stupode* in the world of 150 years from now.'

stupode (stu´pode) | *neol. stupefy.* to deprive of senses. *-ode.* Grk. suffix denoting a thing resembling or of the nature of | *n.* A human transformed into a robot; *(loosely)* any robot; *(colloq.)* an idiot. *v.t.* To convert a human into a robot.

(BELOW LEFT) Howard V. Brown for *Startling Stories*, May 1939. The vehicles resembling caterpillars must be counted among the artist's most convincing creations.

(RIGHT) Cover by Norman Saunders for *Marvel Science Stories* (eventually *Marvel Comics*), April-May 1939. Unrelated to either of the inside stories (only two that month), the painting depicts a beauty *salon* of the future where customers receive a vibratory induced rejuvenation.

(ABOVE) 'A policeman fired at the Tri-Octopus, but the shot had no effect'. An uncredited illustration for a scene in Oscar J. Friend's 'Robot A-1', *Startling Stories*, July 1939. The front cover of this issue, from the same story, is reproduced as the frontispiece in the present book.

(LEFT) Jack Williamson's 'After World's End' was a fine subject for a late colour cover by Wesso in *Marvel*, February 1939. The lack of detail in the poorly depicted two-dimensional ships contrasts oddly with the finish given to the city below.

(RIGHT) Frank R. Paul's April 1940 cover for *Fantastic Adventures* seemed reminiscent of his very earliest work in *Amazing*. Though the figures here seem distinctly better rendered. James Norman's tale of temperate climes beneath Antarctica, 'The Blue Tropics', supplied the copy.

LIFE ON JUPITER

Jupiter's inhabitants would need to be massive, of tremendous strength to cope with the enormous gravity of this giant world. They would probably be forced to a clumsy means of locomotion, since long legs would be impossible. An Earthman would need a tractor car to get about

For complete details, see page 97

FANTASTIC ADVENTURES, JANUARY, 1940

Paul's renderings of imagined life on other planets ran on the back covers of *Fantastic Adventures* for several issues. 'Life on Jupiter', dates from January 1940. The heavy Jovian reptiles have that unmistakeable warmth and humorousness which the artist instilled into so many of his creations. The background architecture, resembling a penguin ramp at a zoo, seems perfectly suited to the life-form.

LIFE ON URANUS

The inhabitant of Uranus lives on a rigorous planet indeed. He is confronted with tremendous gravity, dense atmosphere, poison gases, and great storms. (See page 96 for details.)

A strange bat-like Uranian encased in heavy metallic suiting invites an earthling to come down and see his place. The weird crystalesque growths behind dominate an imposing landscape. 'Life on Uranus' by Paul, *Fantastic Adventures*, April 1940.

116

(RIGHT) Uncredited illustration in the very first issue of *Marvel*, October 1938. An amphibious extra-terrestial takes a peek before deciding whether he should go any further. Women were frequently the object of alien libidos and the sadistic slant here is characteristic of SF pulp sexuality.

(BELOW) Cover of *Science Fiction*, December 1939. Another alien with eyes for our women hot-foots it away with his latest conquest. As soon as the two cops catch him he will be booked for transporting her across state lines.

HIGHWAYS AND BYWAYS IN... MECHANIX!

Futuristic and SF-type illustrations were not limited to *Amazing, Astounding,* and similar publications in the 1930s and 1940s, but were also to be found in magazines which, at first sight, would never have seemed a haven for renderings of imagined technological feats of the near, far, and distant future. These magazines, with such titles as *Popular Science, Modern Mechanix and Inventions, Mechanics and Handicraft,* to name but three — there were many more — were ostensibly devoted to easily understood developments in science, the construction of time-saving gadgets (which seldom saved time but were certainly *gadgets*), and general household do-it-yourself*ary.* Initially they were restricted to such fare but the accent soon shifted to the more wildly speculative — it was better copy, more dramatic — and it seemed that the editor only had to hear of a High School student in Spokane writing to the Secretary of State suggesting that the military equip themselves with aircraft that sucked themselves through the air (on the principles of the vacuum cleaner — from whence the idea) and that the wingspan should be at least 3,000 feet, before the art department had rendered the idea in garish colour and it was spread across the cover with the announcement that — U.S. Government Considers Amazing New Plan! A slight exaggeration perhaps, but this does illustrate the thinking and practice behind these magazines. Articles like 'Signal Light for Babies' Cribs', 'Novel Gate Latch', and 'Fame and Fortune in Sandwiches' (all featured in *Mechanics and Handicraft,* September 1936), as good as they might be in filling out the editorial, hardly lent themselves to graphic interpretation on the cover in the eye-catching and circulation-boosting manner demanded. No, something startling and imaginative was needed. Thus the following ten covers reproduced from this sub-school of pulp publishing. A footnote in the history of SF illustration.

Bulletlike Rail Car
Launches Giant Planes
PAGE 55

At last — a circular runway! The cover for *Popular Science Monthly,* June 1937, by Edgar F. Whittmack, graphically demonstrates the amazing possibilities of this unique and last-word-in-science proposal. 'Racing along a wide gauge track at 150 miles an hour, electrically driven streamlined cars will launch giant transport planes . . .' The aircraft will continue to land in the conventional manner though, thus not rendering the undercarriage obsolete. Just why the planes should be launched this way is considered a minor point not worth explaining. But we are assured that 'the scheme is expected to *overcome present take-off hazards*'! By substituting new ones?

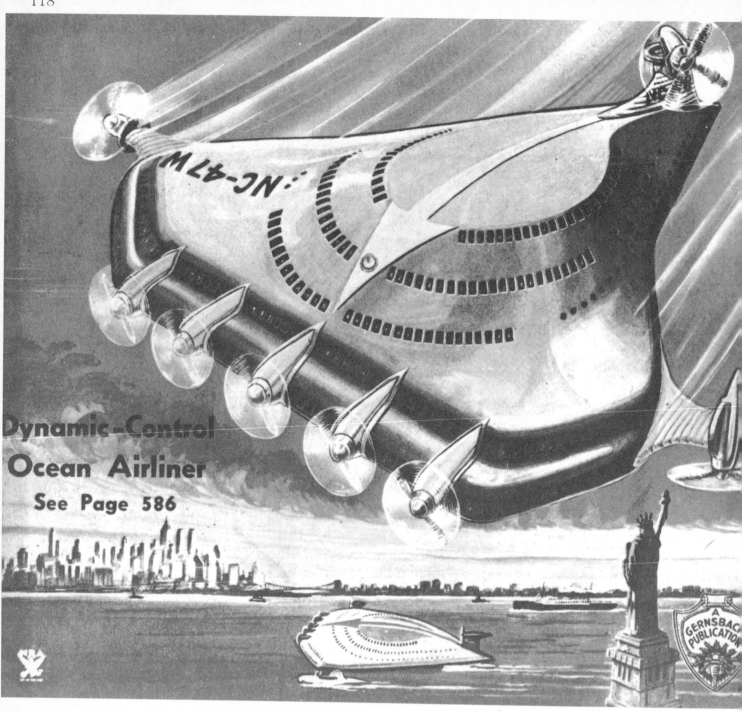

Dynamic-Control
Ocean Airliner
See Page 586

(LEFT) 'Suction lifts planeless aircraft'. Frank R. Paul's rendering of an aircraft which is driven by 'streamlined aerofoils arranged about the periphery of rapidly driven wheels' (in the nose). Hugo Gernsback's *Everyday Science and Mechanics*, December 1935.

(LEFT) The 'Dynamic Control' Ocean Airliner was invented by Gernsback himself and was executed for the cover of *Everyday Science and Mechanics*, November-December 1934, by Paul in inimitable fashion. Some idea of the creation's size can be gauged from the propellers which are over eighty feet in length. Gernsback felt that the ocean liner with wings was a technological possibility, an economical inevitability, and only a matter of years away. He notes that the earliest lighter-than-air craft of the Wrights, which weighed a mere one-eighth of a ton, to the DOX plane of his time, weighing fifty tons, was only a passing of twenty-six years. 'The 10,000 ton airplane, projected on a like time-scale, would, therefore, make its appearance not later than 1952. However, with the nature of the present-day technique, it is quite possible, at this moment, that the 10,000 ton plane will be here much sooner'. The naïvete evinced in this statement compels one to agree with Gernsback's severest critics.

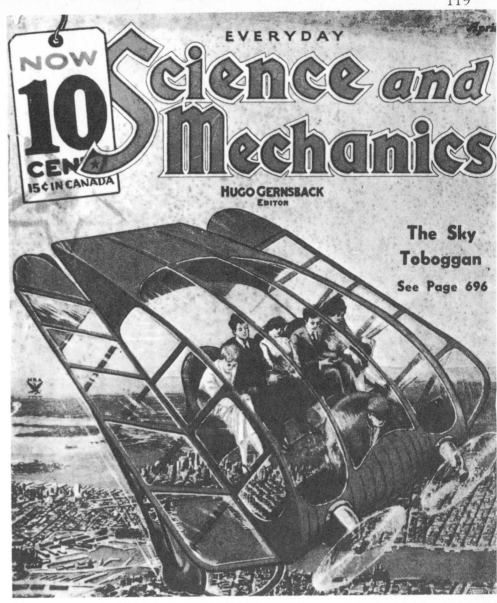

(ABOVE RIGHT) Cover by Paul, *Everyday Science and Mechanics*, April 1935. The Sky Toboggan, actually called the Sky Sled by its inventor, Gene Austin (U.S. Patent No. 1,980,246), could well have been invented by Gernsback himself. 'The transparency of the machine — for observation purposes — is another idea, derived from a foreign source[?], but not impracticable with modern materials'. The craft, we are assured by the copy writer in fine period-flavoured prose, would 'give an interesting ride to thrill-seekers'.

(RIGHT) Uncredited cover artwork showing the proposed combining of a Zeppelin and an aircraft. *Modern Mechanix and Inventions*, September 1935. Among the articles and features of the issue, typical of this kind of publication, may be considered the following:

After Dinner Projects; Watch Fish Grow in this Rustic Acquarium; Glass Cooky Jar become Diving Bell; Flashlight plays Photo-Electric Marimba; Camp Lantern contains Compass; Lawn Mower has Reverse Shift [the present writer's favourite]; Hollywood Stars Become Model Fans; Sturdy Roll Developing Tank Saves Time, Requires Little Solution; and, Idaho's Logs could reach the Moon (says Nick Sprank in Oddities of Science).

Mechanics
AND HANDICRAFT
15¢
JAN.

THE NEXT WAR!

UNDER THE ICE
TO THE NORTH POLE
IN 1937
BUILDING THE PYRAMIDS
A New Prize Contest!

MODERN MECHANIX
AND INVENTIONS
NOW 15¢
IN CANADA 20¢

JA

TANK BATTLES
SEE PAGE 3

STARTLING MILITARY SECRETS OF THE
NEXT WORLD WAR
By PAUL MALLON, Noted Washington Observer

(ABOVE) 'Amphibious tanks that can travel on water as well as land have been developed by several nations'. An uncredited artist shows us what, we are promised, will be the next arrival a 'seagoing battleship with caterpillar propulsion!' *Modern Mechanix and Inventions,* January 1934.

Mechanics
AND HANDICRAFT
15¢
MAR.

THE TRIPHIBION FOR LAND, SEA AND AIR

SKY RIDERS OF THE DAWN PATROL
READING THE RIDDLE OF ROCKS
BUILDING A SEAWORTHY ROWBOAT
THE VENOMOUS VOLCANO
SCIENCE · INVENTION · EXPERIMENTS

(ABOVE LEFT) *Mechanics and Handicraft,* January 1936. Cover artist unknown. The glorification of war technology reaching new heights (or depths). For some, another World War could not happen soon enough.
(LEFT) The 'Triphibion' featured on the cover of *Mechanics and Handicraft,* March 1936, was one of the few proposals from these magazines ever to get off the ground. Well, actually, it didn't — it burst into flames just before its maiden flight, and photographs of the occurence were gloatingly reproduced inside.
(RIGHT) A suggested 'artillery spotter' which, it was claimed, would fly through the air on the same principle as the jelly-fish swims through the water — a pulsating canopy! *Modern Mechanix and Inventions,* February 1936.

MODERN
MECHANIX
& INVENTIONS MAGAZINE
NOW 15¢
Februar

PARACHUTE
ARTILLERY SPOTTER
SEE PAGE 66

Flying the 50-Ton Pacific Clipper

Mechanics
AND HANDICRAFT
15¢

SEPT.

SUPER WAR
TANK

WHAT
TO
INVENT

PORTABLE BARBECUE
•
PLANT SMUGGLERS
•
BUILDING A
SMALL POWER LOOM

NEW PUZZLES CONTEST

Super War Tank! Super Tank! Super War! Great moments in the pornography of violence . . .

This new tank, promised to render every other design obsolete, the ultimate in land iron-clads, is built with two wings, one on either side, attached to 'swivelling yolkes'. The wings are normally folded back flush with the side of the tank's body, but can be brought forward for battle. Should they encounter an obstacle they are elevated in order to clear it, thus not hindering advance.

Each wing is additionally supported by bullet-proof tires and the backs are completely open to allow 'the machine-gunners to drop to the ground and charge the enemy at the opportune moment'.

The uncredited cover for the September 1936 *Mechanics and Handicraft* (but why *Handicraft*!!??).

Appendix Two

SMALL AD CHARIVARI.

It was largely the ads, both small and display, which festooned the opening and closing pages of the American pulps that gave any idea of the outside world — an outside world of the *now* rather than the future — let alone what was happening there. While it is true that the Second World War featured prominently, as indeed it did in everything up to and including *The Young Lady's Crochet Companion Monthly*, such events are unique in the life of a nation both in terms of physical and emotional mobilisation. And should one examine just how SF regarded the War, the approach will be seen to have been as another pretext for the mayhem of the Higher Technology ('Adam Link Fights a War') and little else.

For a genre which prided itself on contemporaneity and awareness, though one increasingly realises this was restricted solely to science in the abstract, the insularity is hard to forgive. Of course, one would never have expected *Spicy Mystery Stories* or *G-8 and His Battle Aces* to argue over the finer points of the New Deal, they readily admitted to being nothing more than thrills and spills, yet SF which did make claims failed to live up to them.

This is not the place to sift the evidence for charging SF with escapism but the point should be made that fretting over the problems the twenty first century might have in attempting to harness ESP (or what you like) *in 1974!* is surely comparable to fawning over sub-Morris (William, that is) tales of chivalry while you sip meade and drop acid under an oak tree at the foot of Glastonbury Tor.

The ads, then, were the unacceptable face of reality, mainly political and commercial, jostling its way into the marbled corridors of Science. The selection reproduced here, divided between those reflecting the Depression, the sexual knowledge (or lack of), and the usual indispensable household gadgets and similar, afford a firsthand reflection of the period. Place yourself in the position of the unemployed man to whom the job ads may well have held out the only hope — '$70 a week, *even in times like these*' …

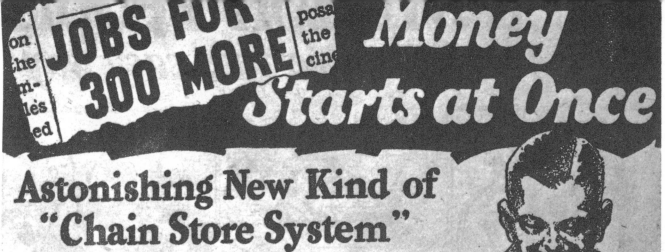

JOBS FOR 300 MORE

Money Starts at Once

Astonishing New Kind of "Chain Store System"

Pays Men and Women up to $70 a Week!

Even in Times Like These

GROCERIES   DRUGS

THEIR Confidence was Justified

WHEN 169 RAILROADS FAILED IN 1893, JOHN H. PATTERSON SAID:

"The year has been unparalleled in the history of the United States. Great questions were to be solved, every industry was stagnant. Some closed down, some lost courage, while a few pushed ahead and worked harder than ever with confidence in the future. We did not let the hard times interfere with our work. When times got duller, we advertised the more and worked the harder."

WHEN PIG IRON DROPPED 50% IN 1907, ANDREW CARNEGIE DECLARED:

"This panic will soon run its course and pass away leaving no impediment to the return, in due season, of another period of wholesome, because needed, expansion of our resources. . . .

"We have had the greatest expansion of modern times. Reaction had to come—will prove healthful. Nothing can stay the rapid progress of the Republic. She is all right."

WHEN DEEP, DARK GLOOM RULED IN 1921, THOMAS FORTUNE RYAN SAID:

"Our merchants have been buying only what they can sell quickly for cash. The consumer has had to listen to so much pessimistic talk that he buys only what is absolutely necessary. People everywhere have been scared. They are getting over that.

"Our people are the greatest consumers of food and manufactured articles in the world in normal times—and normal times are coming back. . . ."

AMERICA CAME THROUGH!

In 1893 stark ruin stalked through the land. 467 banks failed in a few months. Mills, furnaces and factories shut down everywhere. Bankruptcy was on every hand. America had twice as many unemployed per thousand population as she has today. But she put them all back to work.

In 1907 panic broke loose. The production of pig iron dropped 50% in less than a year. All but the strongest men lost heart—"We are ruined," they declared, "recovery cannot come in our time." Yet in two years prosperity had returned.

In 1921, when many honest and thoughtful people were predicting worse conditions, the country was already beginning to climb to the greatest era of prosperity it had ever experienced.

History tells how America has fought and won 19 major depressions. Good times always follow hard times, as surely as day follows night. Prosperity always comes back. It is coming back *this* time, too.

Above all things, let us have faith.

America Has Beaten 19 Major Depressions
She will Beat this one

$200-$250 MONTH
SPECIAL AGENTS (Investigators)
Government Secret Service Work is one of the most fascinating and interesting branches of the service for men. These positions are located throughout the country and are both traveling and stationary. In addition to the high salaries that run up to $5000 yearly, all traveling expenses are paid while on the road.

$2100 YEAR TO START
CUSTOMS INSPECTORS
The duties are to check and inspect goods brought into this country by tourists, merchants, and manufacturers. Inspectors are required to levy the duties etc., and see that Customs regulations are not violated. This is a very fascinating work with splendid salaries.

$1400 TO $3000 YEAR
RURAL and CITY CARRIERS
The Rural Mail Carrier is out in the open air and sunshine; easy, healthy work, short hours, with a large part of the day left to do as he pleases. Thousands of city positions available for those who prefer inside work, delivering mail to large office buildings. These positions available to both country and city people.

$1500-$1860 YEAR & UP
MEAT INSPECTORS
This is very interesting work. Farmers, butchers, or anyone with a knowledge of live stock, food products, meats, etc., are in line for one of these positions. The salaries and promotions are based on the ability and interest shown in this work.

$1260-$1680 YEARLY
CLERKS—STENOGRAPHERS—TYPISTS. Both Men and Women
Pleasing, steady work with opportunities for rapid advancement, up to $2500 per year. These positions may be had in the various Government Offices at Washington or in any part of the country. This also includes Forest and Field Clerks.

DO IT NOW

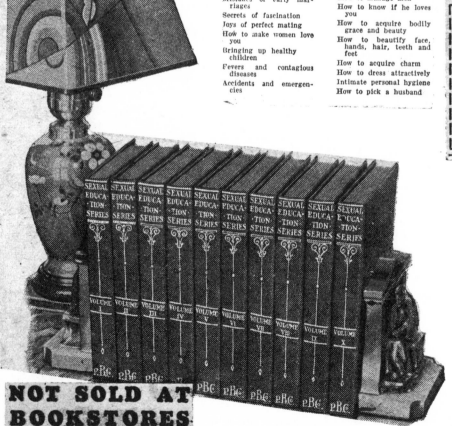

Though not a crank, I would like to express my objection to female characters in your stories. I thought WONDER STORIES presented science-fiction, a thought-provoking type of literature that was unique and different from the hackneyed fiction? Yet the inevitable girl of this latter fiction pollutes the otherwise excellent narratives of our cherished WONDER STORIES, a feature which I consider as wholly detrimental to ever attaining popularity among intelligent circles. Whilst it must be acknowledged that of late there has been a welcome increase in the number of stories with no female characters, it is by no means yet complete.

This was the year 2002, and you didn't rejoice when a beautiful girl said she'd be your bride!

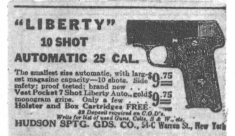

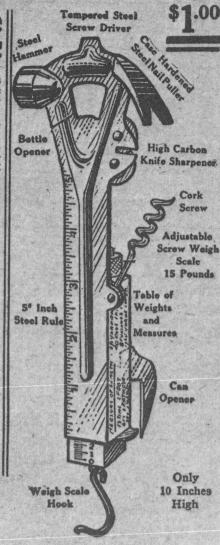